V. Hancke

PREHISTORIC
LIFE ON EARTH

PREHISTORIC
LIFE ON EARTH

by Kai Petersen

Edited, adapted and supplemented by
GEORG ZAPPLER
Department of Zoology, Columbia University

Illustrated by
VERNER HANCKE

LONDON
METHUEN & CO LTD
36 ESSEX STREET WC 2

First published by Politikens Forlag in 1957 as
FORTIDSDYR I FARVER. All rights reserved
First published in Great Britain in 1963
Printed in Holland by the Ysel Press, Deventer
Catalogue No. 2/2680/1

Contents

The history of the development of life from its very origins up to man in the Atomic Age has been divided into geologic time periods. The main divisions are called eras. Several eras mark the course of earth history prior to the beginning of the fossil record; these are all lumped together as Pre-Cambrian times, which are believed to have lasted 2,500 million years. Next come the Paleozoic, the Mesozoic, and the Cenozoic Eras, in that order. Each of these is again subdivided into periods, beginning with the Cambrian, about 500 million years ago, and which marks the occurrence of the first fossils. Suppose we try to visualize this incredible span of time as being twelve hours. That would make Pre-Cambrian times from midnight until almost 10 o'clock in the morning. The big Mesozoic reptiles called dinosaurs don't appear until after 11 o'clock, and man delays his appearance until twelve seconds or so before noon. The last five thousand years, when man gave up stone tools and began to learn the use of metals, founding the well-known ancient civilizations, represent but a small fraction of the last second of the twelve hours.

THE CALENDAR IN THE ROCKS

Rock and stone have always been among the historian's most reliable sources of information.

Egypt's ancient history speaks from the decoratively coloured stone walls of the Pyramids; the Assyrian kings chiselled their bloody deeds on the brick walls around the palaces of Nineveh and Assur; Titus immortalized the destruction of Jerusalem in the marble reliefs of the triumphal arch of the Capitol; the runic stones of Scandinavia tell in simple words the tale of deeds performed thousands of years ago.

Time never stands still. Generation followed upon generation; empires rose and disappeared again—but the stone outlived them all.

But long before Rome's legions stormed the Holy City, long before Pharaoh's slaves dragged stones to the mausoleum of the Son of Ra—in fact, hundreds of millions of years before Man had even shown himself upon the surface of this globe—Nature had begun to write her own saga, engraving it into the crust of the Earth, piling up her manuscripts like numbered pages in a book.

This exciting, action-filled tale of adventure about strange worlds long extinct is told by the fossils—the remains of animal and plant life in prehistoric times.

There has been knowledge of these fossils since time immemorial. During the Stone Age they were already being used as ornaments and amulets, and their strange appearance has caused wonder throughout all ages and given rise to the most remarkable of conjectures. To this very day Chinese pharmacists sell pulverized "dragon's bones" as a reliable cure-all for any form of sickness, from a toothache to sterility.

But historic evidence is of little value unless its language is understood. Ancient Egypt was a closed book until the riddle of the hieroglyphics was solved, and it was not until a Danish archaeologist, C. J. Thomsen, thought out the connection between man and the curiously shaped flint stones which from time to time turned up beneath a farmer's plough that historians seriously began to penetrate beyond papyrus rolls and Babylonian clay tablets.

The correct interpretation of fossils is also a recent discovery. The hunters of the Ice Age from the caves of southern France naturally had no idea what their amulets represented. Admittedly the Greek natural philosopher Xenophanes was able to give a correct explanation as far back as about 500 B.C., but nobody paid any particular attention to him. The learned heads of ancient times regarded fossils as weird manifestations of Nature's whims, and ordinary folk naturally associated the fossilized bones of giant prehistoric animals with the Cyclops mentioned in Homer and other fantastic creatures from the classical world of deities.

Christianity's political victory in the fourth century A.D. and the adoption of Biblical tradition as the highest authority in matters of natural science proved disastrous for European research—a Babylonian captivity which was to last a thousand years. Fossils were regarded as being the remains of casting moulds which had originated from rejected attempts at creation, and a Swiss professor voiced the contention as recently as in 1726 that a fossilized giant salamander was nothing but the sad remains of "a poor sinner that drowned in Noah's Flood."

The great universal genius of the Italian Renaissance, Leonardo da Vinci, who in all fields was in advance of his times, understood the true facts of the

Georges Cuvier, who turned the study of fossils into a science.

matter around the year 1500, but otherwise they did not begin to dawn on the world until the Danish scholar Niels Steensen—or Nicolaus Steno, as he preferred to latinize his name—arrived at Malta in 1664.

The rocky little island in the Mediterranean had become famous for the curious tongue-shaped stones found all over the island. These were a good source of income for the inhabitants. The feeling of insecurity due to the perpetual wars of those days had created a tremendous market for good-luck amulets, and the Maltese "tongue-stones" were for some reason or another particularly in demand. They were so popular that a smart archbishop in Mainz made a fat profit out of selling imitation "Malta tongues" to soldiers who sought his aid.

Niels Steensen was the right man to lift the mystic veil. He had just completed a thorough study of the anatomy of sharks and immediately saw that the

Niels Steensen, who through his work gave impetus to modern geology.

strange "tongues" were quite simply fossilized sharks' teeth. Their widespread occurrence on the island of Malta he explained by the fact that the island must have been previously covered by the sea—a conclusion which seems very natural today but which in the seventeenth century was a revolutionary break with the then prevailing belief that the division of land and sea had been laid down once and for all since the creation of the earth. In addition, Steensen also had very original ideas about the principle of succession in overlying rock strata.

In 1669 Niels Steensen published his theories in a little pamphlet, the appearance of which, in the opinion of many scientists, marks the birth of modern geological thought. The pamphlet was apparently intended to be the draft of a larger work, but this never materialized. Niels Steensen possessed the brilliant perspicacity that is unhampered by traditional theories but not the stubborn energy of the true research worker. A single problem could not, in the long run, retain the interest of his turbulent mind. Furthermore, a few years later science lost the benefit of his great talents. He became seized by religious scruples and abandoned his work at the University of Copenhagen.

It now became the turn of the French naturalist and research worker, Georges

Three typical fossils. On the left: an ammonoid, the size of a tractor wheel. This was a shell-covered animal distantly related to the squids and now extinct. Top right: a so-called "thunderstone," really a preserved sea urchin. Below: a trilobite, representing a group which 500 million years ago were highly successful forms of life.

11

Cuvier, who, around the beginning of the nineteenth century and as the first to do so, made fossils the object of a systematic, scientific study and thereby founded **paleontology.**

Professor Cuvier performed a meritorious service by introducing the results of **comparative anatomy** as a basis for the reconstruction of the appearance of prehistoric animals. Based on the study of living forms, it can be shown that all bones and organs have their own special features in narrow relationship to the particular species, size, etc., of the animal in question. This is naturally of tremendous importance to paleontologists, who often only have fragmentary parts of skeletons to work with, but can thus infer with some confidence conclusions about the over-all constitution of extinct animals. Today paleontologists have recorded over 100,000 extinct species of animals, and new species are continually being brought forth from the hidden archives of the Earth's crust.

Even so, we only know an infinitesimal fraction of the total number of animal and plant species which have ever lived on Earth. In the first place, an almost improbable coincidence of fortunate circumstances needs to take place in order for an animal to be preserved in the form of a fossil after death, and, secondly, fossilized material is, as a general rule, difficult to get at. The majority of discoveries in the past have been due to pure chance. Scientific search in selected areas is a relatively recent development.

The reason for this meagre representation of the actual fauna in the fossil record is easy to understand. One only has to go for a walk in the country. Thousands of animals die every day. Their corpses should be lying around everywhere.

But how often does one stumble over a dead animal or even part of a skeleton in a field or wood? Almost never! In the economy of Nature little is wasted. Hardly has an animal collapsed to the ground before the demolition squads move into action. Carrion feeders, including myriads of insects, set to work on the body, and billions of bacteria complete the work of decomposition. The bare bones crumble beneath the effect of the sun, the air, and the acid soil, and in the course of an incredibly short space of time there is nothing left.

It is only when the body is covered immediately after death with a protective layer, such as clay or gravel, for example, which shields it from the oxygen in the air and other destructive agents, that there is a possibility of avoiding the total disintegration which is otherwise the inevitable fate of life that has expired.

This does not mean, even under these

An unmistakable plant impression now preserved as a mould in the surrounding rock.

favourable conditions, that the whole animal will be preserved. Such has only happened in extremely rare cases, and

The scene as it may have appeared during a volcanic eruption 25 million years ago.

then usually in the more recent geological periods. The soft parts normally decompose rapidly, even when buried, and only the hard parts of the animals, such as bones and shell, scales and armour plating, are left, their original elements often being partially replaced by mineral compounds made available through the seeping action of water. Plant fossils are generally found as carbonized remnants or as impressions in stone. These fossils, however, are often so excellent that even the cellular structure of their tissues can be studied under a microscope.

It is obvious that the process of fossilization has the greatest chance of taking place under water, where a body can sink deeply into the mud or quickly become covered with ooze, and therefore we have a lot of information concerning the now extinct inhabitants of the oceans, rivers, and lakes. This applies not only to fishes and numerous invertebrate animals, but also to other animal groups which live wholly or partly under water, or which occasionally go into the water —e.g., amphibians and reptiles, and mammals such as whales and seals.

Confirmed terrestrial animals, on the other hand, have but small chances of being preserved as fossils after death. The possibility is greatest in very dry regions like deserts and steppes, where the dry atmosphere can preserve the skeletons for a longer period and the desert sand and prairie dust blows over them. Valleys, inland basins, and the mouths of rivers are usually the best localities for fossil finds because the upland areas, even if they contain fossils, are eroded away with the passage of time.

Natural catastrophes which took place in former times are of the very greatest

Plaster cast of a dog which was buried under volcanic ash during the eruption at Pompeii in 79 A.D.

importance in providing material towards the excellent fund of knowledge which, in spite of everything, has been acquired concerning extinct animal life on land.

Forest and prairie fires have driven large flocks or herds of animals out into lakes and rivers, where many of them have drowned or become trampled to death, and sudden floods have resulted in similar massacres. Earthquakes have opened fissures and crevasses forming convenient mass graves for many animals. Volcanoes too play a considerable part.

It is well known that frequently at the start of a volcanic eruption the boiling column of steam from the crater produces a tremendous cloudburst. This rain, mixed with the tremendous mass of ash thrown up into the air at the same time, pours down in destructive torrents of mud and in a moment is capable of wiping out all life over large areas. It was a colossal burst of ash-rain such as this from the volcano Vesuvius which in the year 79 A.D. buried the cities of Herculaneum and Pompeii in southern Italy. Historical research several centuries after the catastrophe revealed a priceless gift: two ancient Roman cities petrified like the Sleeping Beauty's Palace in the midst of daily life. In the same way the ravages of volcanoes millions of years ago have produced and preserved rich material for study by scientists of our day.

Excavations in fossilized ash masses give, moreover, many touching proofs of how life's manifestations have remained unchanged over the course of millions of years. In many places it has been possible to reconstruct how terrified animals have cowered together in small groups, pressed up against each other while mass death rained down on them from the sky.

Other prehistoric animals are known to us because they met a cruel death in swamps and quagmires. One such example is the tar pits which existed in western North America a few hundred thousand years ago and which are famous as cemeteries of the creatures then living. Springs of petroleum bubbling to the surface formed viscous ponds of tar whose treacherous surface was disguised by blowing sand. Some of these pits are still active today. Unsuspecting animals were sucked down, and their hard parts became preserved in the asphalt which formed as the tar hardened. Frightful dramas must have taken place in these oil swamps when colossal creatures such as elephants, and sabre-tooth cats attracted by this helpless and hoped-for prey and now trapped themselves, fought for their lives in the sticky morass. Vultures swooped down on the defenceless animals, and the sound of their beating wings must have mingled with the resounding trumpet blasts from the elephants, the snarling death roars of the sabre-tooth cats, and the howling of the dire wolves along the banks.

Today the old oil lakes are scientific gold mines. Thousands of animal skeletons have been dug out of the asphalt, and there remain incalculable numbers still.

Incidentally, fossils are not necessarily petrified. They can be preserved in their original composition. All traces of animals and plants found in layers of earth older than twenty to twenty-five thousand years are called fossils. It is not the state of preservation that is the deciding factor, but solely the geological age. Organic remains in present-day formations are called **sub-fossils.**

Thus a specimen of a woolly-haired rhinoceros was discovered in a tar swamp in Galicia in a wonderful state of preservation, complete with skin and hair, just like a regular mummy. This was due to a waxy film of hydrocarbon completely enclosing the corpse. Commonly known, too, are the frozen mammoths of Alaska and Siberia. These Arctic mummies were so well preserved that, although the animals died many thousands of years ago, when they were found they looked almost as though they were alive. Unfortunately they begin to decompose as soon as they come into contact with the air. The famous roast joint of mammoth which was supposed to have been served

This 20,000-year-old woolly mammoth was found in Siberia—solidly frozen and completely preserved. The drawing is of a cast at the Leningrad Zoological Museum.

15

Prehistoric North American tar pits were often death traps. Here both the prey, a now-extinct elephant, and the hunter, a sabre-tooth cat, end up in one of those treacherous oil swamps. The vultures are gathering for a meal.

at a banquet given for a scientific congress in Moscow is only an amusing cock-and-bull story. In practice it would be an impossibility—even in Russia.

Lumps of amber are sometimes found that contain fossilized insects. Although it may have been millions of years ago that the insect was caught in the drop of thick resin which later turned to amber, the observer has the feeling that it will begin to flutter its wings the moment he sets it free from its yellow prison.

In cliffs, footprints have been found which have been made in the distant past by an animal treading in soft earth, and which thereafter have remained untouched while the soil, over the course of millions of years, has been transformed into solid rock. Preserved pieces of excrement also form part of the material used by paleontologists, and fossilized reptile eggs containing scraps of embryonic bones, over a hundred million years old, have also been found.

Thus our journey through these long-lost worlds does not lead through a trackless waste. Hordes of strange animals— often more grotesque than human fantasy can conceive—stand like milestones along the route. An unbroken parade from the awakening of life until today is, however, more than our present store of evidence is capable of presenting. Our knowledge of the most recent periods of the Earth's history is naturally the most complete. The farther back we seek, the more difficult does it become.

We have only opened a small number of the fossil treasure chambers concealed in the crust of the Earth, and the richest of them probably lie inaccessible, buried at the bottoms of the oceans, although new scientific methods are now beginning to explore this region also.

Furthermore, a great number of former fossil beds have been completely or partially destroyed. The deeper structure of the Earth's crust is never at rest, and the forces which now and then cause it to shake and tremble were far more violent than now at certain periods during those far-off times to which we shall be giving our consideration.

These periods of violent upheaval of the earth's crust are recorded in today's rock formations. Frightful earthquakes literally turned many earth strata, and with them any contained fossils, upside down, crushed them, folded older layers over on top of younger ones, and from below the Earth's crust molten streams of lava broke through to the surface, wiping out any trace of fossilized life in their path.

Less dramatic, but just as important in terms of loss of fossil material, are the slow processes of erosion that go on constantly. As certain rock strata are uplifted and then worn down again by the action of sun, wind, and water, any preserved animal and plant remains in them will of course be lost to future discovery.

But although many gaps are thus still waiting to be bridged, we are able, nevertheless, with the help of fossils, to form an idea of the main lines of evolution which lead from ourselves—the self-crowned lords of creation—back through untold millions of years to the very lowest branches of our tree of descent—or phylogenetic origins.

A lump of amber with a fossilized insect.

THE STREAM OF LIFE

If we take a look at the documents provided by the fossils in the Earth's
strata in their geological sequence—this
sequence also indicating a succession in
time—we can form a clear picture of the
way life has changed through the ages.
Life is like an unbroken stream, whose
outer pattern has, so to speak, been constantly moulded by the demands set upon
it by the ever-changing environmental
conditions to which it has had to adapt.

The tree of life has its roots and early
shoots in the waters of the oceans. Deep
down at the bottom of our pile of fossil
"documents" we only find life *below* the
surface of the sea. The land areas are
barren, stony deserts. However, most of
the major groups, or phyla, into which
living organisms are divided, had already
appeared. There were simple plants,
single-celled animals, sponges, jellyfishes, snails, many kinds of worms, and
primitive representatives of the group to
which starfishes belong. The vertebrates,
which are only one phylum among about
fifteen others (all invertebrates), are not
recorded until somewhat later. For many
millions of years forms related to crustaceans and insects and relatives of the octopus and squid were the most highly diversified creatures on our globe. Later the
fishes deprived them of some of their supremacy, but the earliest vertebrates which
gave rise to the true fishes were primitive
beings without jaws and with poorly
developed fin structures. In the next act
of vertebrate evolution the scene shifted
to the land, where the **amphibians** were

the first to appear. The first amphibian,
with its fishlike body and imperfect
limbs, points clearly towards an ancestor
that had abandoned its natural element.
However, it was not until the appearance
of the **reptiles** that life fostered a genu-
inely terrestrial vertebrate group, which
for a hundred and fifty million years
dominated not only the land and the sea
but also the air above. The mysterious
collapse of the reptile dynasty handed
their throne to some small hairy animals,
and sixty to seventy million years ago
these, the **mammals,** which had existed long before that time, were able
to commence the grandiose development
that was to culminate in man as one of
their many lines.

Often the fossil record shows that individual classes of animals have enjoyed
a flourishing period of power and thereafter have been replaced by a new and
possibly better adapted group. At the
same time there is undeniable indication
that the "deposed" assemblage has itself
fostered the successors to the throne at
one time or another in their history.

The first amphibians resembled fish,
and the first reptiles resembled amphibians. The first mammals and birds had
unmistakably reptilian features, and the
first human beings shared many characteristics with apes.

The present level and rich variety of
species of life on Earth must therefore
have been the result of a never-ceasing
evolution from "lower" towards relatively higher forms. Only a few animal types,

such as the sponges, jellyfish, and sea lilies, for example, have continued their existence almost unchanged from their first appearance up to our times. None of the major groups have become extinct, but many individual assemblages within these phyla have had a limited span of existence. They flourish for a time and then disappear when drastic changes in world conditions, combined with an inability of their hereditary mechanisms to produce the necessary modifications to survive under the new conditions, put a stop to their further development. Many of the animals which at the present day lead an obscure existence had proud forebears. The lobster's distant relations were once the globe's most terrible carnivores; frogs and newts are directly descended from the first conquerors of the mainland; tortoises and lizards represent but small remnants of the former dominance and diversity of the class of vertebrates known as reptiles.

Today the domination of the land that had been shared by many different types of mammals has been taken over by a single species—man. However, we cannot blame ourselves wholly for this impoverishment of the world's fauna—many species of elephants, rhinoceroses, giraffes, etc., common only one million years ago, had already died out before man's overwhelming population increase added so greatly to the extermination of the large mammals of the world. Only the rodents seem to have profited; if we can call this the Age of Man, we can with equal justification relabel it the Age of Rodents. We certainly cannot predict what evolution holds in store for man. We do know, however, that biological and—with man—cultural evolution is a continuous process destined to continue.

Life's journey, as seen in the light of evolution, from a hypothetical molecule in the primeval seas to present times.

The concept of evolution is today just as natural as the idea of the global form of the Earth. The majority of civilized human beings have long since accepted the gorilla and the chimpanzee as "poor" relations, and only very few feel distaste at the thought that our branch on the phylogenetic tree far back ran into that of the crocodile, the spider, and the starfish.

However, it was not until the latter half of the last century that the Biblical legends concerning Creation began to give way to a scientific outlook on the origins and evolution of life. Even in the late nineteenth century excellent geologists and biologists really believed that men and all creatures had been created just as they are today from the very beginning.

Gradually, as the number of known species of animals increased by new thousands, people here and there began to speculate concerning accommodation problems in Noah's Ark. But even with the rise of these and many other doubts, there was still opposition in principle to giving up the constancy of species as the dogmatic basis of zoology. It had natu-

rally been observed that animals resembled one another mutually to a greater or lesser degree, but then allowance had to be made for the limits to the imagination and ingenuity of the Creator. To attribute to these similarities an actual relationship based upon common descent was at any rate held to be quite absurd.

Even Georges Cuvier, the father of paleontology, was convinced as to the immutability of species. From his study of fossils he knew that the animal world had changed character several times and formerly was completely different from that of the present day, but the reason for this he did not see in a transformation of the individual species. It was due, in his opinion, to world-embracing natural catastrophes which at certain intervals had wiped out every living thing on Earth, after which life had spread forth again by means of a new act of creation.

Cuvier's observations seemed to support the **catastrophe theory,** as it was

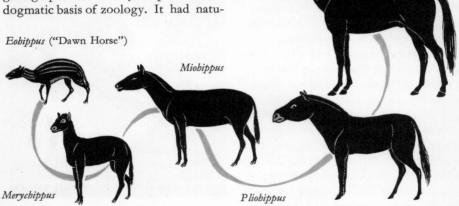

Eohippus ("Dawn Horse")

Miohippus

Merychippus

Pliohippus

Equus (Modern Horse)

Some representative forms along the evolutionary line leading to the modern horse—starting with the sheep-sized and forest-dwelling *Eohippus*.

called, rather than a concept of continuous evolution. Towards the end of the eighteenth century an Englishman by the name of William Smith had already proved that breaks appear in the geological sequence, where older strata are directly followed by younger strata containing an essentially different animal world. If the fossilized animal species of these strata were to be brought into developmental relationships, it would be necessary to have clear, transitional forms—and such forms were not to be found. The stratum containing the new fauna lay immediately on top of the older stratum. Cuvier explained these breaks, and particularly the one preceding the appearance of recent forms, in terms of upheavals, similar to the Flood mentioned in the Bible.

Such misinterpretation should be seen against the background of the insufficient material and imperfect geological knowledge available to him at the time. Cuvier did not realize that the sharp difference between the collections of fossilized animals in two adjoining strata is due to the fact that in the interim between the two layers the underlying stratum is often uplifted and laid bare to the destructive forces of the elements, becoming eroded. By the time it once more subsides and new layers are deposited on top of the old ones, either in the sea or in inland basins, many millions of years have passed, and only naturally the animal life has had time to become completely different. Also, the transitional forms may not have lived in the same area as did their ancestors or later descendants. Thus they might be missing from a localized geological section.

The fossils in long, uninterrupted, successive strata clearly show the gradual transformation of organisms, and today many of the intermediary stages which Cuvier missed are known. Transitional forms have been found which build a bridge between such widely separated classes of animal life as reptiles and birds, reptiles and mammals, and between many other apparently widely separated groups. From more recent geological periods we can—in the case of horses and elephants, for example—assemble an almost complete series of intermediate forms which show step by step how these animals have acquired their present appearance.

Ideas about the existence of evolution in nature, rather than static concepts of a nonchanging universe, started with some of the ancient Greek philosophers. However, it was not until the eighteenth and nineteenth centuries that these notions were again entertained by the scholars of the time. Many of them accepted evolution as a basic trend and hypothesized about possible mechanisms. To mention just a few, there were Spinoza, Leibnitz, Schopenhauer, and Kant discussing these things on a purely speculative level. People like Goethe in Germany, Buffon and Saint-Hilaire in France, and many others from all over Europe were making some attempts to collect scientific evidence for a theory of evolution. Actually, though, it was not until Jean Baptiste Lamarck's publication of his *Philosophie Zoologique* in 1809 that any professional zoologist came out wholeheartedly for evolution as the general explanation of the history of life.

Lamarck's work, in spite of what are now recognized as fundamental errors, was the first concentrated attempt to put forth a scientifically-founded theory of evolution and to explain the beginnings of now living species as a result of the alteration

Jean Baptiste Lamarck, whose ideas were scorned by the scientists of his day.

of organisms over the course of time.

He laid most stress on some inherent, mysterious tendency for life to progress from the simple to the complex. Since life does not really follow such an ideal progression from the less perfect to the perfect, he explained away this inconvenient fact by saying that the "true" course of evolution is hindered by individual adaptations. He used as evidence the well-known fact that organs which are used most develop most powerfully, while those that are little used degenerate; the muscular arms of the blacksmith and the frail body of the tailor are the classic examples. Lamarck assumed, as had everybody before him, that offspring inherited the qualities which the parents had acquired in this way, and thus he attributed the existing state of organisms to their having altered their anatomy in this fashion. His later adherents modified his theory to state that changing conditions in Nature carried with them alterations in the manner of living and should

gradually be able to produce new species. According to them, individual modifications were caused by the reactions of organisms to the direct influence of external conditions.

Philosophie Zoologique suffered a sad fate. The scientists of the day swept it aside as a simple figment of the imagination, and Lamarck died in poverty and obscurity.

It was partly his own fault. Logical consistency was not Lamarck's strong line, and his conclusions were throughout too easily arrived at and loosely founded. Many were much too fanciful to be taken seriously. Thus he asserted that the giraffe had acquired its long neck thanks to its forebears having continually stretched out after the foliage at the tops of trees, and that snakes had originally been newts which lived in narrow cracks in the rocks where their limbs got in the way and therefore eventually disappeared. His explanations why birds have feathers and snails have horns seemed even more ridiculous, and the first zoological work to be produced on the theory of evolution was drowned in the scornful laughter of the professors.

Posterity has recognized some of Lamarck's important contributions but has not been able to accept his and his followers' basic ideas. That changing conditions and biological evolution are related is certainly true, but not in the direct fashion pictured by Lamarck's school. Lamarck's conception of the inheritance of the acquired qualities has proved to be entirely erroneous. The son of the blacksmith does not necessarily have to be born with more powerful muscles than the tailor's boy, and notwithstanding the blind man's more acute sense of hearing, his children, born with normal sight, do not therefore hear better than other people. A scientist chopped off the tails of a mouse family over several generations without ever producing a tailless mouse, and although Chinese women have mistreated their feet for centuries, the practice has never resulted in deformed children.

The neglect of Lamarck by his generation was due mainly to Cuvier's bigoted attitude on the subject of evolution and the over-all misconception scholars had about the period of time that was available for evolution to have occurred. Quite simply, nobody believed that the Earth was old enough. Most people estimated its age at about 6,000 years. This remarkable figure originated from an Irish archbishop who, with the help of the genealogical tables of the Old Testament, worked out that creation had taken place on October 26, 4004 B.C., and moreover—with admirable precision —was able to fix the exact time of the ceremony as having been at 9 o'clock in the morning. In some way or other this nonsense ended up in an official English Bible and was accepted the world over as fact. In Lamarck's time a few wise heads had expressed their doubts concerning the worthy archbishop's arithmetical abilities, but as regards the main principle, scientific research was chained to the idea of a young Earth.

It was not until 1830 that the English geologist Charles Lyell, a former barrister by profession, in his large work *The Principles of Geology* upset all the notions of time hitherto conceived by geologists and reckoned the duration of the various epochs, marked by the deposition of rock strata, in terms of millions of years rather than the hundreds assumed before him. He dated the production of the different types of minerals, plants, and animals so far back that the units of time accepted by his predecessors shrank, by comparison, to seconds. Building upon the work of Steensen, the Dane mentioned before, and Smith, the Englishman, he used the principle of geologic succession to date various rock strata by means of the characteristic fossils contained in them. Since the younger rocks overlay the

Charles Darwin—
the father of modern evolutionary theory.

older ones (in undisturbed sections) and since the same types of fossils can be found in contemporaneous layers, it becomes possible to establish a geologic chronology. By calculating, from available data furnished by present-day processes, the enormous length of time required to build up sedimentary layers, carve out stream beds, and form other geological features, this chronology could be demonstrated to be built up of units of millions upon millions of years.

The same year that Lamarck's *Philosophie Zoologique* saw the light of day in Paris, a man was born on the other side of the channel who, fifty years later, was

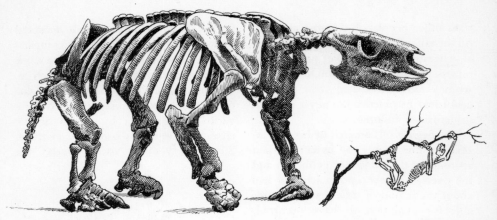

A comparison between the skeletons of an extinct South American giant ground sloth and the closely related living tree sloth.

to lead evolutionary theory to a splendid victory. The man's name was Charles Darwin, and as he himself has acknowledged, Lyell's pioneering geological concepts gave him the proper time perspective from which to observe nature in such a manner as to lead him to his renowned final synthesis.

Darwin's interest in natural science awoke at an early age. At his father's urging he had initially studied to become a physician and later, losing interest in medicine, he tried his hand at theology at Cambridge. There he came under the guidance of geologists and zoologists who urged him to take an unsalaried position as the naturalist on board the English man-o'-war *Beagle* which was to make a five-year voyage of investigation around the world. That was in 1831 and Darwin was twenty-two-years old.

The young Darwin started out believing that all the various animal species had existed from the very beginning, but his experiences during the *Beagle's* world cruise engendered doubt in his mind. On the Galápagos Islands, situated off the coast of South America, he observed how the bird and reptile species of these

islands resembled one another, with all of them showing clear-cut resemblances to South American forms, but nevertheless they varied distinctly from island to island. It seemed to him absurd that a special animal community should have been created for each island, but the whole thing became understandable if the animals were descended from the same mainland stocks and had merely developed in different directions after having been isolated on the individual islands. In Argentina Darwin saw the fossilized skeletons of tremendous prehistoric animals which strikingly resembled that country's existing armadillos and sloths, only much larger. Why were the extinct giants and their contemporary counterparts only to be found in South America? All this seemed to point to the fact that the existing species had the same origins as the extinct giants.

In other places, too, Darwin observed the existence of many species with a small area of distribution, representing many forms closely allied, but not alike, and taking the place of one another in different localities. Thus while the prow of the *Beagle* clove through the waves of

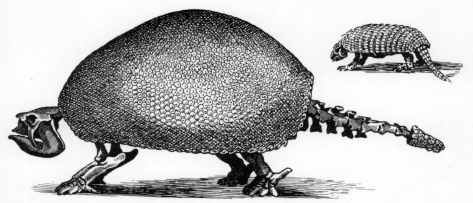

The skeleton of the now extinct South American giant armadillo compared with its present living descendant.

the oceans, his doubts concerning the immutability of species rose to certainty. Species were not constant entities, but rather they were modifiable. The mutual similarities of animals must be due to a blood relationship based on common descent.

When Darwin came home to England he immediately set about sorting out his tremendous material and collecting new data, but it was not until 1859—after more than twenty years' industrious work—that he produced his epoch-making treatise *The Origin of species by Natural Selection*. Even then he thought he was "rushing" the job but felt he had to publish due to his friends' urgings.

The book caused a tremendous sensation. His theory of evolution was not only accompanied by an overwhelming number of established facts gathered from plant and animal life and domestic animal breeding, but Darwin's theory of **natural selection** gave at the same time a convincing explanation of the driving forces behind evolution. These were not dreams of fantasy but the results of an honest scientist's sober and reliable labours.

Darwin's name flew round the world. Many biologists welcomed his ideas with admiration. The problem appeared solved. Some few protested, but mainly for reasons of personal envy rather than intellectual doubts. Certain religious circles stormed against the "ape theory", but times had changed since Lamarck's day, and a scientific theory could no longer be easily swept aside by quotations from the Bible. Incidentally, the religious hullabaloo was doing Darwin a grievous injustice, for he remained a professed Christian throughout his life and never dreamed of intruding upon religious teaching. He had deliberately kept the origin of man out of *The Origin of Species*. That was not to come until 1871 in his book *The Descent of Man*.

In 1882 Charles Darwin was able to die confident in the knowledge that his theories were finding ever-increasing support, and England laid her renowned son to rest among the other great men of the nation in Westminster Abbey. Posterity has had to correct the great pioneer on important points, but in principle his theory of natural selection remains unshaken.

25

HEREDITY AND SELECTION

Natural selection is the fundamental principle in Darwin's theory of evolution. Darwin felt that in nature a merciless struggle continually rages for the necessities of life. Here it is a question of the survival of the fittest. The weak will sooner or later be destroyed, and only the strongest and most fit will survive the struggle and live to influence evolution. Inspiration for his theories he had very significantly obtained from a book on political economy by Malthus. This work discusses how both in nature and in human life there are produced individuals in far greater quantity than there are means for maintenance, and how the weak therefore perish in the competition for food.

The struggle for survival, however, is hardly as dramatic as Darwin portrayed it. In reality this competition is not so much a bloody war to the death as it is a statistical struggle, where the best adapted will tend to produce more offspring than the less "fit"—thus eventually causing those hereditary characteristics which have made them the "fittest" to predominate in the population. But in principle Darwin was right.

If the number of living beings were in true proportion to their procreative powers, the world would rapidly become an impossible place in which to live. A herring lays thirty thousand eggs annually, and tapeworms over a hundred million; likewise, a single mouse family could overpopulate the Earth in less than a hundred years. It is obvious that the greater part must perish. Neither politics nor social welfare offices exist in nature, and an animal is lost if it is unable to find sufficient food for itself or cannot avoid persecution by its enemies.

The farmer improves the breeds of domestic animals by using the best livestock for breeding purposes, but among wild creatures Nature herself "selects" the fittest.

Which line selection takes will tend to change with the character of the surroundings, including other organisms, the types of food available, and all other prevailing conditions. The animals that live in Greenland's snowbound wastes are different from those in the Amazonian jungles. Man is, in fact, the only species of animal that has been able to exist in both the freezing cold of the polar night and beneath the burning sun of the Equator. All other animals have to adapt themselves structurally to the demands of the environment, becoming differentiated in the process. One example would be the adaptations for running found in many mammals. Prairie animals are generally graceful and swift of foot. The wide open spaces do not afford many hiding places, except underground, and if a herbivore wants to "succeed", it will have to be able to outdistance its enemies. These, the carnivores, in turn will have to evolve and become more efficient in catching their prey as the latter becomes more adept at outrunning the former, namely its pursuers. One acts, so to speak, as an impetus on evolutionary change in the other—the direction of the impulse being mutual.

This is a very generalized example, and in reality the processes concerned are much more involved and complex. No one single factor, such as efficiency of locomotion, for example, accounts for an evolutionary trend. All the factors in the environment, such as competition for food between animals of the same species as well as between organisms of different species, are important in varying degrees. The lion does not simply compete with other lions for food, but also with all the other carnivores living on the same prey as itself. Various things can happen. Either the lion line "ousts" the other

group—or somehow each type of carnivore will adapt itself to a different niche. That is, they might live together in the same geographical area but will differ, if only slightly, in their requirements. One may, to put it in an oversimplified fashion, hunt giraffes; the other may just hunt rodents. Whereas the one may seek shelter in clumps of bushes, the other might conceivably excavate its own dens. Sometimes when there is an abundance of a certain type of food a number of different carnivores will feed off the same prey. But in times of stress, that is, when the supply of food becomes limited, such as might happen if an epidemic decimates the population preyed upon, each type of carnivore is able to change its habits in a different fashion. For example, one may eat carrion; another may switch to robbing the poultry yard; another might leave the stricken area; yet another will produce fewer young that particular year, thus "stretching" available resources, and so forth.

Examples of camouflage. The greenish stick-insect, the yellow butterfly, and the stoat in its white winter pelt, all show how form and colour tend to make their possessors blend with their usual background.

Examples of the effects of isolation. These various East Indian birds of paradise all had a similar ancestry. However, the various stocks being isolated one from the other developed their own distinctive features, each one now being a recognizably different species.

Camouflage plays an important part in Darwin's argument. He stressed heavily the astonishing ability animals have to merge with their surroundings—or **cryptic colouration.** Thus the polar bear is as white as the snowy wastes in which it lives; the reddish-brown coat of the lion can hardly be distinguished among the tall savannah grass, and the lurking tiger's yellow stripes melt into the flickering shafts of sunlight in the bamboo thicket. Darwin also pointed out the ability of animals to protect themselves by what is biologically known as **mimicry;** that is, some species can externally resemble animals which their enemies for one reason or another fear and avoid. There are, for instance, species of flies that look for all the world like wasps, while many harmless snakes bear a striking resemblance to the gaudily striped and poisonous coral snakes.

Examples of the role of natural selection. Both types of mice live in the same general area. The white ones inhabit the sandy regions, whereas the black mice are found along the strips of dark laval soil that crisscross the semi-desert.

Darwin did not believe—as Lamarck and his followers did—that the phenomenon was due to the animals themselves or to any direct influence on the part of their environments. But the ability to camouflage themselves gave these animals, in his opinion, a tremendous advantage in the struggle for existence. They were better able to hide from their enemies and could more easily creep up unseen upon their prey, and in the course of time this led to the extinction of the majority of animals that were handicapped in respect of camouflage. Present-day scientists attach considerably less importance to this factor, but its influence is still recognized and has recently been experimentally demonstrated.

Natural selection was the most important and most convincing part of Darwin's theory. He had difficulty, however, in trying to demonstrate the kind of variations among which Nature could choose. Darwin pointed out the fact that no children look exactly like their parents. That cannot be denied, but on the other hand the differences are extremely small, and it is difficult to see how minute variations could lead to the kind of differences found between, say, a sparrow and a hippopotamus. Darwin answered by pointing out the tremendous space of time available to the processes of evolution. Favourable variations are summed up from generation to generation and unceasingly strengthened by continued selection. The first variations had of necessity to be insignificant.

It sounded reasonable. After all, all cumulative change is gradual. Nature is not alone in having a conservative dislike for sudden revolts. The same aversion characterizes mankind's cultural achievements. The first railway carriages were in reality only stagecoaches on rails, and the oldest automobiles were little more than motorized horse-drawn carriages. The motorcycle is a modern example. A few years ago it was merely an ordinary bicycle with a motor attached; nowadays it has its own individual features.

And just as the streamlined diesel engines and chromium-plated cars of our days bear little resemblance to their clumsy antecedents, the majority of present-day animals only vaguely remind one of their distant forebears. The first horse did not have only one hoof to each foot; the first rhinoceros had no horn, and the first elephant had neither a trunk nor tusks.

Darwin also realized that there might be such a thing as overspecialization. A particularly well-adapted animal might become so very dependent on a highly specific environment that should the situation change suddenly there would not be sufficient time for enough variations

Gregor Mendel, founder of the modern theory of heredity—or genetics. The value of his work was recognized only after his death.

to occur that might be selected out to make the organism's descendants fit for the new environment. That line then might become extinct. A creature adapted to only one particular kind of food, such as the Australian koala (the original inspiration for the teddy bear) which eats only eucalyptus leaves, will do very poorly if this plant disappears. On the other hand, a more generalized herbivore, not "committed" to such a specialized mode of life, will have a better chance of surviving under new conditions. Selection is always in the direction of the best adaptation possible, but since the environment is never constant, the terms "best" and "most fit" are highly relative —what is "best" today may be less so tomorrow. What originally began as an advantage could thus in time become a

drawback, and this fitted in with Darwin's ideas concerning Nature's self-regulating accidental occurrences better than with Lamarck's belief in purposive development towards some perfect ideal.

Still Darwin approached Lamarck's views on the influence of living conditions. The theory of selection depended upon the favourable variations Nature was able to select and whose features were inherited by descendants. Darwin himself found no satisfactory explanation as to how the variations arose, and he attributed some of them to the inheritance of acquired characteristics in the same way that Lamarck did.

He knew that his ignorance on the subject of heredity formed the weak link in the chain, but he probably remained unaware that this was in point of

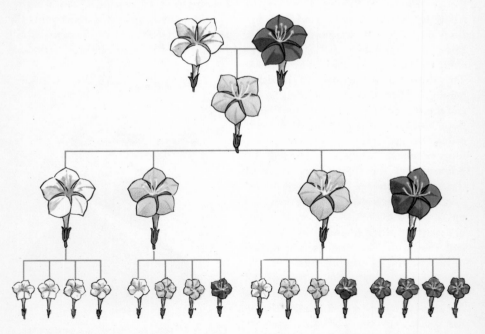

The principles of Mendelian segregation and recombination are illustrated by breeding experiments with the four-o'clock plant.

The protruding chin of the Hapsburgs has been a dominant feature of their line for over six hundred years. The gene determining this characteristic must have been passed on unaltered from generation to generation. There is no dilution effect such as might be expected from a theory of heredity based on the "blood mingling" concept.

fact his Achilles' heel. He even went so far as to propose a provisional theory of heredity which rested on the concept of a mixing of parental traits in the offspring that was soon to be shown to be completely wrong.

For, in a quiet monastery garden in Brünn, the Austrian monk Gregor Mendel created a new science: **genetics.** He experimented with crosses between different types of the same plant with the idea of discovering an explanation for the behavior of such hybrids and thereby finding a fixed law of heredity.

Mendel removed the veil from secrets which had hitherto been kept hidden. His experiments with cross-fertilization produced many strange results, but the monk's alert mind understood how to work out the true answer. He worked with peas, but we shall use the four-o'clock plant *(Mirabilis)* as an equally good example. Thus if a white-blooming plant is crossed with a red-blooming variety, the result is a cluster of pink hybrids. That is understandable if we think in terms of a mixing and diluting effect. But if the pink *Mirabilis* hybrids are then pollinated with each other, the third generation comes to consist of white, red, and pink flowers in a quite definite ratio. If thereafter the white and red plants are kept "pure", they retain their colour constantly in all subsequent generations, whereas the pink plants continue to pro-

duce multicoloured offspring in the same proportion as before. There is no permanent dilution effect then; the trait for a particular colour, even if outwardly obscured, remains "uncontaminated" in the hybrid—since some of its offspring will show the characteristics as strongly as ever the grandparents did.

Such **Mendelian segregation,** or the ability of hereditary traits to survive unchanged in hybrids, cropping out again in definite and predictable ratios in the second generation obtained by crossing

Professor W. Johannsen, famous Scandinavian geneticist.

these hybrids, is the basis for the science of heredity. However, in addition to simple segregation, there is the factor of **dominance** which was also discovered and described by Mendel in his work on the genetics of peas. Dominance is the phenomenon whereby the expression of a given trait in the hybrid may be influenced more by one parent than the other. In the case of the four-o'clock plant the hybrids of white and red parents were pink — both parental contributions to the colour trait thus had equal expression — neither one dominated the other. However, often this is not the case. A brown-eyed woman, who has received the trait for brown eyes from both parents, and a blue-eyed man will have only children with brown eyes. The blue-eye colour is **recessive** towards the brown. Still these particular brown-eyed children retain the ability to pass on to their offspring the blue-eye colour, inherited as a recessive trait from their father.

This will occur if they marry someone who has either blue eyes or who is a brown-eyed "hybrid" like themselves. In other words, for blue eyes to be outwardly manifest a double contribution — one from each parent — is necessary. Brown eyes, on the other hand, will be possessed by people with either a single or a double hereditary determiner. As to which kind of brown-eyed they are can only be seen from the offspring they produce.

Hereditary features then are independent units which are received and continue unaltered. An offspring receives definite tendencies both from the father and the mother, but they are passed on independently of each other. The individual determiners are constant and do not fuse together with others.

Hugo de Vries, the first to point out the importance of mutations in the process of evolution.

Mendel's laws also explain how a whole family can keep a characteristic feature, such as a big nose, for example, or a prominent chin. It is a matter quite simply of a dominant trait which remains undiluted despite the fact that the family, through the marriage of its members, continually receives new hereditary qualities from without.

For Darwinism the results of Mendel's experiments were of necessity shocking, to put it mildly. If new individuals, deviating from their parents in respect to hereditary qualities, were an impossibility, then natural selection could have no material with which to lead development along new lines. Now Mendel had come along and proved that nothing could be produced by heredity that had not existed beforehand. Even in hybrids all that had occurred was a regrouping of already existing features. There was, literally speaking, nothing new under the sun, and therefore any form of development must be unthinkable. The minor hereditary variations on which Darwin had based his whole theory appeared not to exist.

The monk from Brünn nevertheless did not bring the theory of evolution through natural selection into difficulties. In 1865—six years after *The Origin of Species* was printed—he produced his results in a small natural science magazine published in Brünn and only read by a small minority, of whom even fewer understood the far-reaching importance of Mendel's experiments.

Darwinism continued its victorious path unmolested throughout the world, and Mendel died in 1884 without seeing his merits acknowledged. That was not to come until much later—but when it did a stately marble monument was erected in front of the peaceful monastery garden.

A few years before the turn of the century a Danish plant physiologist, Professor W. Johannsen, began to experiment with beans. He wanted to try to produce new strains by means of consistently sustained selection, and in order to exclude the errors introduced by working with mixed material he cultivated the seeds of every bean separately. Within each "pure" line of progeny thus produced he found that there exist certain types of hereditary units—which he called **genes**—that remain unchanged throughout. If the plants are starved, both they and their seeds become small; if they are manured, they grow strongly —but this has no effect upon the hereditary character. Whether one sows large or small seeds of the same pure line, one obtains under the same external conditions the same plant type. There is thus within one and the same pure plant line a certain unalterable hereditary **genotype**, as Johannsen called it, whether or not the environment alters the external form of the individual, or the **phenotype.** Actually the genotype can be defined as the sum total of the self-reproducing units of the organism, whereas the phenotype is the end result of the interaction between the genotype and the environment. The units called genes segregate according to Mendelian ratios. The individual, as such, is then the product of its genotype reacting with all the conditions under which it is produced and lives: nutrition, climate, temperature, nature of the soil, etc. However, what is heritable is not this phenotypic result but only the hereditary unit factors, the genes, which are constant and are transferred unchanged (although they may be recombined) from generation to generation.

This clear-cut demonstration that acquired traits are not hereditary seemed like a stumbling block to the theory of evolution by means of natural selection. If the hereditary material is completely fixed, how can the variations from which the "best" are selected occur and how are they passed on? Seemingly, then, there were no hereditary variations.

The highly conservative nature of genetic processes having been demonstrated, it remained for a Dutch botanist, Professor Hugo de Vries, to demonstrate that Darwin's variations did occur after all and that these were hereditary.

In a fallow field outside Amsterdam, De Vries found two types of evening primrose, which were quite different from the general appearance of the majority of these plants, growing there in abundance. He took some of these last home and planted them in his garden.

Within a short time he began to get the variations he had noticed before. The new types when raised separately bred true. He therefore felt that he had finally demonstrated the existence of the hereditary variations long sought after by students of evolution, and he called them **mutations.** His contribution was a milestone in the development of evolutionary theory, but ironically enough, although mutations were later clearly demonstrated to exist, his particular primrose variations turned out to be simply due to latent recessive characteristics and were not really mutations at all.

Individuals then are capable of two types of variations: those produced by the environment to yield the phenotype, but which do not affect the basic genotype—these are not inherited; and those changes in the genotype itself which are replicated in the offspring. These last, the mutations, which occur completely at random and independently of the environmental situation, are the building stones of evolutionary processes. It is these that are filtered and screened out by natural selection.

Through the work of Professor Morgan of Columbia University and his students the nature of mutations has been very much clarified. In experiments with fruit flies it could be demonstrated beyond doubt that such hereditary changes occur relatively frequently and in all size ranges from almost unnoticeable minor variations to very radical alterations indeed.

All living creatures—apart from one-celled plants and animals—are built up of an incredibly large number of tiny cells. Each cell contains a central body, called a **nucleus,** on which the life of the cell depends. Scientific research has clearly demonstrated that the hereditary units or genes are aggregated into groups called **chromosomes.** These are rod-shaped bodies located in the nuclei; their number is constant according to the species (human beings, for example, have forty-six), and they always reduplicate themselves faithfully whenever a cell divides into two. The genes making up these chromosomes not only determine whether the individual is to be a fish, a wasp, or a human being, but also decide details such as the breadth of the yellow stripes on the wasp's back or, in the case of human beings, colour of hair, shape of nose, etc.

The chromosomes are passed on from generation to generation, usually within specialized germ cells called **gametes,** from which the individuals of the new generation develop. When the male gamete, or **spermatozoon,** enters the female gamete, or **ovum,** fertilization occurs. The two nuclei merge, one with the other, and it is at that moment that the hereditary make-up of the offspring is determined. Both parents contribute to an equal extent, since the gametes only contain half the number of chromosomes characteristic of all other cells in the body. Thus, at fertilization, the species specific number is restored. This process of sexual reproduction, which is found, to some extent at least, in almost all animals and plants, thus serves not only to create a new generation, but also permits a reshuffling of the genetic material of the parents. The halving of the chromosome number during gamete formation is a random process, so that the combination of the two sets (one from each parent) in the offspring differs from that in either parent. This is very important since it provides many minor variations among the individuals of a given species. Such differences, in addition to the more important genetic mutations, can also be selected for in the course of evolution. Then too, if a favourable mutation occurs, it can be more readily passed throughout the whole population if each individual is the result of a random shuffling of two parental sets rather than a mere duplication of a single parent. This last is the case in asexual reproduction, a process of which some species are capable in addition to the sexual method. (There are some organisms that only reproduce asexually—but they are comparatively rare.) When a plant cutting becomes a new plant, or when an amoeba simply splits in two, the resultant individuals are genotypically *exactly* the same as the parent—unless a mutation has occurred. Such exact duplication is never the case in sexually produced progeny, no two of which (unless they are twins developed from the same egg) are exactly the same.

Precisely what happens when a gene mutates is not yet known. Actually it is still unknown what a gene is, except that it must be a unit in the chemical make-up of a chromosome. A mutation, then, is a change in the structure and composition of such a unit. We do know that genes are inherited as discrete units, but in development they act as interacting and co-operative sets. Thus single genes may affect different structures, or a single character may depend for its development on a number of different genes.

Experiments with fruit flies and other organisms have shown that an increase in the normal and spontaneous mutation rate can be provoked by means such as X-rays, ultra-violet rays, poisons, and excessively high or low temperatures. Radioactivity has the same effect, and as the great majority of mutations are harmful, this is the basic reason why many biologists have protested against the exploding of hydrogen bombs; they are afraid that increased radioactivity will cause catastrophic hereditary results on human life.

Scientists can thus provoke mutations, but does this therefore mean that they can direct the progress of evolution? No. They can increase the frequency of mutations by artificial means, but they have not the slightest control over the hereditary displacements provoked. Mutations take place completely blindly, without purpose, and independently of surroundings and the demand for changes. If biologists experimented with human beings instead of fruit flies, it would be an act of daring comparable to a few nuclear scientists setting off a hydrogen bomb without knowing whether it would fizzle out like a damp firecracker or blow the whole world into the air. Mutant innovations are pure guesswork.

Most of the mutations noted that produce viable organisms—both inside and outside the laboratory—are of a minor rather than a drastic nature, and this has evoked certain objections as to their importance to evolution. It is hard to conceive, for example, how a stumpy suggestion of wings in an organism that has had no wings before should prove of value in the "struggle" for existence to the extent that subsequent generations would have the opportunity of developing proper instruments of flight. The point here is that these stumps may have served quite a different purpose initially than they did later in evolution. They might have been used as stabilizers of some sort in a jumping or gliding animal

—and only later would true flight develop. We shall see in later chapters that there are many examples of change in function of like structures in related organisms. Often, too, the particular structure which later becomes so very important starts its development not because it itself is being selected for, but rather because the mutation which determines its development also causes other hereditary changes. These other variations are the ones which are being "preferred," and they might be of such a nature that we could not outwardly detect them. For example, the ability to digest food more efficiently could conceivably be related to horn growth. Thus horn growth might not be important in the beginning (or possibly might never become important selectively), or it might become—once the horns have attained a respectable size—an additional and significant factor as far as selection is concerned.

Old accounts point to the fact that mutations of far-reaching significance have been observed in recent centuries. Thus **Mauchamp** sheep are supposed to be descended from a lamb born in France in 1828 with unusually long and silky wool, and a strange male lamb with short bent legs like a dachshund—born in North America in 1791—is supposed to be the progenitor of the **Arcon** race. This strain was bred because it could not jump over fences, and thus this particular heriditary deformity constituted a labour-saving device for the sheep-raising farmer. However, none of these mutations produced distinct species in the true sense of the word. All these strains are still sheep of the same species as their forebears and are only maintained as separate types due to the agency of man.

The problem of how new species are formed will be discussed in the next chapter. For now it will be sufficient to realize that in the process of evolution mutations of sufficient importance must have taken place so that they could have been able to lead life along new paths.

One of the burning questions of the past and to some extent even today is whether the mutations that have led to new forms are sudden major alterations or merely minor changes that are cumulative over the tremendous span of time available. At this point we must distinguish between the relatively small differences found among related species and the tremendous structural gaps that exist between the larger groupings, such as, say, between a bird and a fish. As we follow the fossil record we can, in many instances, see clearly that what is now a seemingly unbridgeable difference started out millions of years ago as a relatively minor variation. However, many links have still not been found, and this has led some scholars to postulate that all the mutations that are important in terms of leading to big evolutionary change are of a major kind. This has been called **saltatory** (or jumping) evolution. Most

Arcon sheep, believed to be descended from a peculiarly short-legged male lamb born in North America in 1791.

paleontologists would not agree with such a hypothesis. They feel that just as an accumulation of minor differences can lead to a new species (this can be observed and studied among present-day organisms), so also can a similar additive effect lead ultimately to major differences. There is no doubt that some of the features which make us distinguish between various large groupings often appear quite suddenly in the fossil record. However, this can be explained by supposing that a rapid series of minor changes was taking place in small isolated populations, specimens of which would have a small chance of becoming preserved. Such a concept is backed up by modern studies on the genetics of populations. These have demonstrated that gene changes would have a greater chance of becoming rapidly distributed and "fixed" in all the individuals of a small population than in one large interbreeding group. The difference between some of the gradual series leading from one type to another and the sudden appearance of entirely new forms is very probably only a difference in the speed of establishment of mutations. However, in both examples the mutations that do become established under appropriate external conditions are not drastic in their effect on the organism. Since any living creature is a very complex arrangement of interacting processes, most acute changes will irreparably damage the efficient working of the whole system. Only relatively minor variations seem to be able to make an organism still function "normally" even if the environment becomes different. Conditions never alter to the extent that a deformed cripple has the "advantage". Since it is one of the postulates of natural selection that

only those mutations become established which lead their possessor to propagate himself more efficiently, thus producing more offspring than the individuals not possessing this particular variation, only a well-functioning and integrated organism will be the one selected for. From what we know of mutation rates and the establishment of "neutral" and advantageous traits within populations, all the kinds of differences we find today among living things can more reasonably be attributed to a piling up of small changes rather than to sudden evolutionary "jumps".

As mentioned before, by far the majority of mutations, be they major or minor, are not improvements. If the evolution of life has continued—and there is no doubt that it has and still does—the instances of successful adaptation due to the proper hereditary change must be attributed to extraordinarily rare, fortunate mutations, and one begins to get an idea of the enormous time periods spanned by the history of life.

Furthermore, the value of a mutation depends first and foremost on the nature of the environment. A reduction in size of an insect's wings would probably be a distinct detriment in a quiet valley, but, on the other hand, such a change could be very advantageous on a stormy, rocky island where small flying forms tend to be carried away by the winds. Changes in climate, which in the history of the Earth are a frequently recurring phenomenon, might have the effect that formerly unimportant, perhaps even harmful, mutations suddenly prove to be gainful and now exert a dominating influence on evolution because the previously well-adapted individuals of the species do not thrive as well under the new conditions, and the mutant carriers gain the advantage.

Mutation and natural selection thus work hand in hand. One is meaningless without the other when we are talking about evolutionary change. Throughout untold millions of years mutation and selection have combined to produce a seemingly oriented effect from a series of blind and random changes.

THE CLASSIFICATION OF THE ANIMAL KINGDOM

The animal species now living represent evolution's terminal for the moment. The immense variety of forms makes an almost overwhelming impression. Zoologists know of over one million different species, and the true figure is believed to be nearly double this.

It would therefore be impossible to survey the profuse multiplicity of life without a means of classifying both modern and extinct animals, and here the concept of evolution gives a logical background for a natural system which sorts the animals into groups according to the degree of their mutual relationship or, more precisely, their biological distance from a common starting point. The system naturally embraces plants too.

The basic unit is the **species,** and closely related species form the **genus.**

The dog, the wolf, and the jackal constitute independent species within one genus, and the same applies in the plant world, for example, to black currants, red currants, and gooseberries. All human beings now living belong to the same species, *Homo sapiens,* a member of the genus *Homo,* in which a prehistoric man such as the Neanderthal man *(Homo neanderthalensis)* represents another species.

The next step in this system is the **family.** Mice and rats belong to the mouse family together with voles, lemmings, and muskrats. Families are grouped into **orders,** which again are arranged into **classes.** The mouse family is placed in the order of rodents, where we meet the squirrel family among others; rodents in turn are members of the mammal class, together with other orders such as that of the primates (which includes monkeys, apes, and men).

The classes are grouped together into **phyla** (singular **phylum**) which—apart from the final division of all living things into the **plant kingdom** and the **animal kingdom**—are the largest units of the system, and embrace the groups of organisms which, from an anatomical standpoint, have one or more very fundamental characteristics in common (such as, for example, a common plan of over-all body organization).

The phylum **Chordata** (or vertebrates) includes all mammals, birds, reptiles, amphibians, and fishes—animals which, though widely different among them-

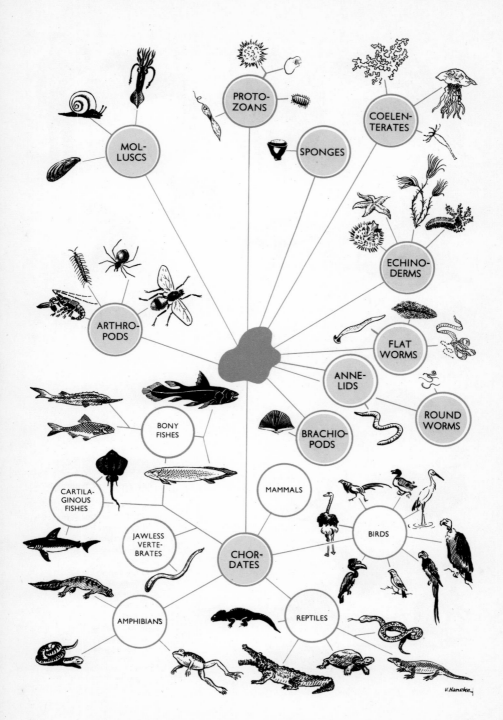

MOL-LUSCS

PROTO-ZOANS

SPONGES

COELEN-TERATES

ECHINO-DERMS

FLAT WORMS

ANNE-LIDS

ROUND WORMS

ARTHRO-PODS

BONY FISHES

BRACHIO-PODS

CARTILA-GINOUS FISHES

MAMMALS

BIRDS

JAWLESS VERTE-BRATES

CHOR-DATES

AMPHIBIANS

REPTILES

V. Hanske

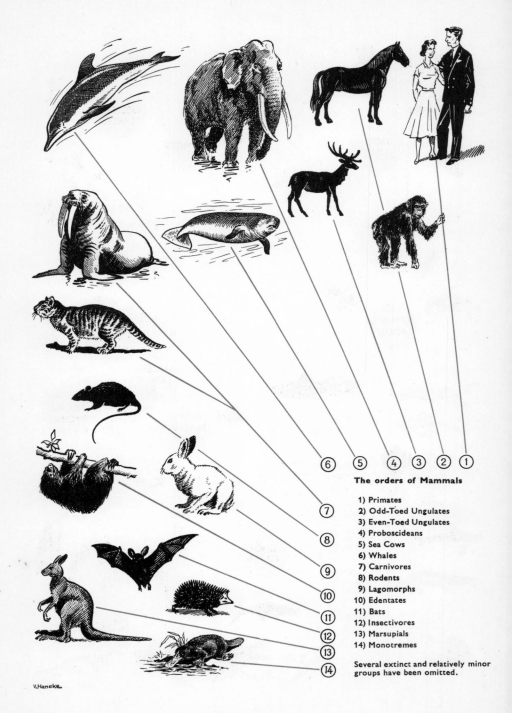

The orders of Mammals

1) Primates
2) Odd-Toed Ungulates
3) Even-Toed Ungulates
4) Proboscideans
5) Sea Cows
6) Whales
7) Carnivores
8) Rodents
9) Lagomorphs
10) Edentates
11) Bats
12) Insectivores
13) Marsupials
14) Monotremes

Several extinct and relatively minor groups have been omitted.

V. Hancke

selves, nevertheless belong together because they all have an internal supporting rod (the notochord, which later in evolution becomes the vertebral column), with an overlying nerve cord, and gill slits, at one time or another in their development. Other phyla are formed by echinoderms (starfishes, sea urchins, etc.), coelenterates (jellyfishes, polyps, sea anemones, etc.), flatworms (flukes, tapeworms, etc.), segmented worms (earthworms, etc.), molluscs (snails, squids, etc.), arthropods (crustaceans, insects, spiders, etc.), as well as others.

A distinction is often made between the **vertebrates,** which comprise only one phylum and include some of the most highly organized representatives of animal life, and the **invertebrates,** which represent all the other animal phyla, some of which have been mentioned above. In a way this is an unfortunate distinction if considered as a division of the animal kingdom. The various invertebrate phyla are often as distinct one from the other as they are from vertebrates. Also, the notion that invertebrates in general are less complex than chordates in general is erroneous. Many phyla among the invertebrates contain representatives that are just as highly organized as are some of the chordates — these again contain many relatively "simple" forms. The insects, for example, do not have to stand behind a mammal in physiological complexity. Their plan of organization is entirely different, however, and it is only natural that we tend to associate ideas of "high" development with the group to which we belong, namely the vertebrates.

Vertebrates and invertebrates—which are all built up of a large number of cells —together comprise the **Metazoa** (or multicellular animals) as contrasted to the unicellular animals or **Protozoa.** Here belong amoeboid organisms, such as the amoebae, the foramineferans, and others, and many groups of flagellated and ciliated entities, most of which are of microscopic size. These protozoans have all their life functions gathered into a single undivided unit, rather than being built up of many different kinds of cells the way the Metazoa are.

When we speak of animals as being "higher" and "lower" forms, we should bear in mind that these terms have real as well as only relative meaning. A descendant form is always higher on the evolutionary time scale—i.e., chronologically it is younger. However, this does not necessarily indicate a "higher"—in the sense of "better"—degree of development. Both ancestor and descendant forms are well adapted to a particular environment. Since evolution is a historical process, all that has gone before has to influence what is occurring and will occur. Instead of "high" or "low", we can talk about *different* levels of organization, each level building upon a preceding one, so to speak. Each of these is really the "best" under a given set of circumstances. Should these change, the flexibility of life is such that some forms may in the process of adapting themselves attain another level. The one-celled amoeba, for instance, appears a relatively simple mechanism. It possesses neither lungs, kidneys, digestive organs, blood circulatory nor nervous system and reproduces itself simply by splitting into two parts. Still, all the needs that these specialized organ systems fulfil in the "higher" forms, namely the exchange of oxygen and carbon dioxide, removal of wastes, assimilation and transport of food, and appropriate reaction to the environment, are nonetheless well taken care of; the machinery is less impressive but still wondrously efficient.

In many of its structures the human being is far more "primitive" than many animals. The hawk has sharper eyesight; the dog has a better sense of hearing, and the horse can run faster. These animals have specialized in a particular manner of living through emphasis on the development of certain features. Man has remained a rather generalized mammal — except for his grasping hands, bipedalism, and the enormous development of the brain. The hawk, for instance, would perish in a dark cave, and the horse could never survive in dense jungle. Man, on the other hand, can better survive a change in his environment, not only by reason of his superior intelligence, but also because from a physical standpoint he commands a greater reserve of adaptability.

Apart from cases of identical twins, no two persons in the world are completely alike (in their genotypes, that is), and among other species completely identical individuals are never met with either. Within the individual species many variations can occur. The difference between a Scandinavian and a Hottentot is, after all, quite considerable.

It is therefore difficult to limit the term species in an obvious and well-defined manner.

The requirement that all individuals within a species must resemble one another in regard to all essential characteristics is no clear definition, for what are essential characteristics? On the other hand, against the background of evolution, it is only to be expected that flexible boundary lines will exist, and it be-

comes difficult to define the term species in just a few words.

Perhaps the concept of what a species is will become clearer if we start with a discussion of what a race is. Species can be subdivided into different races, each one of which can be defined as an interbreeding population of individuals which share in a common "gene pool". Each such **Mendelian population** is a unit of evolutionary change. Races become different for adaptive reasons; for example, pigmentation differences among humans are probably related to living successfully in different climates. Such differentiation is due primarily to **geographical** separation. If two populations live in the same area, interbreeding would obliterate any differences in the composition (that is, relative frequency of certain genes) of the gene pool. With races, then, the maintenance of genetic differences is possible only if they remain spatially isolated from each other. However, organisms belonging to different species can live next to one another and yet retain their specific differences. Here, then, we are dealing primarily with **reproductive** isolation. We might say that speciation is an adaptive process which permits *different* organisms to be neighbors without sharing genes. How is such reproductive isolation brought about? It is made possible by genetic mechanisms. These may vary all the way from causing a complete prevention of fertilization between two individuals of two different species to producing offspring which appear fairly normal but which are sterile or are otherwise "unfit" for reproductive purposes (e.g., the mule). A species, then, is an interbreeding population of individuals, all the members of which resemble one another to the extent that they are capable of sharing in the same gene pool, but which differ recognizably from individuals belonging to other such interbreeding populations and with whom they are incapable of producing fully fertile offspring.

Race formation always precedes species formation in that geographic isolation is necessary for enough genetic differences to accumulate between the populations separated, so that a later coming together will not lead to interbreeding and therefore an obliteration of differences.

The dividing up of the animal world into groups was begun long before Darwin led evolutionary theory to victory. The obvious similarities and differences on which the grouping was based were simply not regarded as denoting degrees of blood relationship.

Aristotle, the great Greek thinker who lived in Athens around 300 B.C., was the first to draw up a zoological system. It covered 520 animals found in Greece or Greek waters. He divided them into "blood animals" (vertebrates) and "bloodless animals" (invertebrates), and each of the two main groups was subdivided into four sub-groups: the blood animals into mammals, birds, amphibians (including reptiles), and fishes, and the bloodless animals into cephalopods, crustaceans, shellfish, and insects.

Aristotle came to have an enormous influence on European science—an influence by no means in reasonable proportion to his knowledge which, after all, was incomplete. It was due, however, to the circumstances reigning after the break-through of Christianity.

In the Church's infancy natural science was regarded as a sin comparable to adultery or stealing. After all, Christianity sprang up in circles where book learning was in sad straits, and the general opinion was that man should solely mortify his soul in preparation for the Day of Judgment. Any source of information outside that provided by the Old and New Testaments was felt to be superfluous, and any further inquisitiveness was regarded in the light of sinful thoughts inspired by the devil.

Obviously this sort of outlook strangled all desire to conduct research, and when the Day of Judgment obstinately refused to come, and an interest in nature revived, a start had to be made from scratch. Aristotle and other ancient writers had been hibernating unnoticed in the Arab world, including Moorish Spain, and their works now became the spring where Europe sought to quench its reborn thirst for knowledge. Aristotle was certain of success, for all his natural

Aristotle, the great Greek philosopher, whose rather limited ideas on the diversity of animal life had almost Biblical authority during the Middle Ages.

philosophy is infused with the notion of a mystical divine power which he believed inspired all living things, and his works acquired almost Biblical authority. In the Middle Ages it was believed that the ancient scribes knew everything worth knowing, and therefore there was no call either to continue or check their work. Learned greybeards would hold heated discussions about how many teeth a cow has, but none of them would dream of opening its mouth and counting. Instead, they dug deep into Aristotle's works and tried to outshine each other in making subtle interpretations of the text.

The Roman writer Gaius Plinius, who perished during the eruption of Vesuvius in 79 A.D., also achieved great popularity in medieval Europe. He wrote a thirty-seven-volume treatise on natural history and collected his material, according to his own statement, from over two thousand contemporary works. What he writes is not all nonsense, but nevertheless Plinius spins many a tall yarn. Thus he relates that lions do not eat defenceless women if they humbly crave mercy, and elephants, according to his information, are deeply religious and worship the sun. Such fables made him very popular.

Containing even more misinformation is a collection of "edifying" animal stories from Alexandria entitled *Physiologus,* which in the course of the Middle Ages were translated into most European languages. The Christian symbolism in them was very obvious, and seldom has such incredible rubbish achieved such wide distribution. Traces of this work are still found in our daily speech; for example, we have it to thank for the expression "crocodile tears", for the book stated that the crocodile—touch-

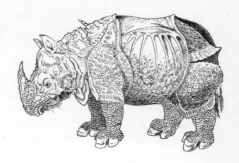

Above: a rhinoceros, probably drawn by Albrecht Dürer, in Konrad Gesner's voluminous work on natural history published in the middle of the sixteenth century.

ingly enough—weeps when it eats people.

The European Renaissance during the sixteenth century gave birth to a new outlook in the natural sciences.

To pick at any of the "truths" established by the ecclesiastical authorities was admittedly to remain a dangerous sport for some time to come. A Spaniard, Miguel Servetus, who had said that the blood ran from the heart to the lungs and back again, was imprisoned in 1553 by the Swiss reformist Calvin and, for the sake of the salvation of his ungodly soul, was burned alive in the market square in Geneva. About the same time the Inquisition took fond charge of the Belgian anatomist Andreas Vesalius, who refused to admit that man had a rib missing on one side (the rib that was used for Eve).

But even so there was an increasing realization of the shortcomings of both the ancient writers and of the Bible as the total sources for an understanding of nature, and people began to try to study the world around them by dint of personal observation—a method not previously considered worth while.

This change in approach naturally had its effects on **systematics,** the science of classification, which furthermore was necessarily influenced by the great sixteenth-century voyages of discovery to unknown shores with their strange animal and plant life.

Konrad Gesner, a Swiss, published a gigantic tome in Latin during the years 1551-58, entitled *The History of Animals,* richly embellished with excellent illustrations. However, Gesner still granted—somewhat reservedly—**mermaids, sea serpents, unicorns,** etc., citizenship in the animal kingdom. These mythological creatures, with which zoology had been blessed for centuries, were not shown the door until an Englishman, John Ray (1627-1705), finally got on their tails. He was likewise the first to try to define the term species based on the requirement that the offspring be similar to its parents, and he clearly brought out the concept that a number of similar species go to make up a genus.

Carl von Linné, the great Swedish systematist.

The systematists, however, had in the main merely patched up the basic framework established by Aristotle. A really consistent system did not exist until a twenty-eight-year-old Swede, Carl von Linné (he afterward latinized his name to Linnaeus), in 1735 published a small, fourteen-page pamphlet: *Systema Naturae* —and became world famous. His "natural system" divided the animal world into **classes, orders, genera,** and **species,** and by 1799 the thirteenth edition had grown into a copious, ten-volume work of six thousand pages in all.

Linnaeus has been variously judged. His contemporaries overestimated him, and when evolution became an acknowledged fact, he was initially underestimated. Linnaeus was not a research worker in the true sense. He introduced order where chaos had reigned but blazed no new trails. However, order and method are so vital to all scientific work that it is his importance in this field which must be recognized if an objective judgment is to be passed.

An inborn sense for systematic organization enabled Linnaeus to complete his classification with strict logic. He was the first scientist of Christian faith to dare to range man among the animals. He placed us together with the apes in his leading mammal group, the primates, where he also included the bats. Posterity, however, has given the bats their own order, and it should moreover be made clear that Linnaeus' comparison of men and apes—and bats—was not due to any assumption on his part of their common descent. He was the pious son of a priest from southern Sweden who believed in the faith of his time and who accepted the constancy of all species without question.

Linnaeus divided the animal kingdom into six classes: **mammals, birds, amphibians, fishes, insects,** and **worms.** Botany, however, was his main field, and Linnaeus' zoological system is poor in comparison with his classification of plants. His last two categories can thus best be characterized as invertebrate scrap heaps, serving to include almost every animal he didn't know anything about. He classified plants according to their reproductive organs which are — at least in the case of flowering plants — concentrated around the blooms. It is said that he considered a similar basis for animal groupings but found that the complications involved were much greater than with plants. He therefore went back to Aristotle's old arrangement and tried to improve on it by using the progressive units: species, genus, family, order, and class, in an orderly and precise manner.

Despite the shortcomings of the system, it nevertheless constituted an orderly basis upon which to work, and with his method of nomenclature, Linnaeus at any rate introduced a reform of extreme importance. He gave all species a two-part designation consisting of a **generic name** and a **specific name.** The domestic cat he thus called *Felis domestica,* and the generic name *Felis* likewise appeared in *Felis leo* (lion), *Felis tigris* (tiger), and *Felis concolor* (puma or mountain lion). (By the way, many of these names have been changed in recent classifications, although all these forms are still grouped into the family **Felidae.**) Linnaeus did not invent this method, but he was the first to employ it with consistency in the fields of both zoology and botany.

Today these binomial designations are used all over the world. They are usually derived from the classical languages Greek or Latin. After all, only a few thousand of the hundreds of thousands of species are commonly known, and it would be an impossibility for each single language to provide a special name for each plant and animal. In this way, too, scientists from all over the world know exactly what animal or plant is being discussed in technical reports dealing with biological matters.

Linnaeus made many mistakes by often classifying according to purely external features. Two species do not need to belong to the same genus because they resemble one another outwardly, and an animal's meaningful (in terms of evolution) characteristics are not always the most obvious. Every organism has to be studied as completely as possible in order to appreciate its relationship to others.

A question as to the most typical characteristic of birds will generally be answered by saying: they can fly. This is not really their distinguishing feature though. To begin with, many birds cannot fly at all (e.g., penguins, running birds such as ostriches, etc.). Furthermore, there are many other winged creatures, such as the insects, bats, and extinct flying reptiles. The special feature about birds is their skin covering of feathers. The possession of wings is shared with many other flying animals. Such similar developments in lines that are not closely related can be ascribed to the process called **convergence.**

Organisms that have had to adapt to similar environments have tended to develop like structures to fulfil similar environmental demands. The fins of certain fishes led to the development of the limbs possessed by land vertebrates.

Two examples of convergence—or the appearance of structural similarities in unrelated forms, due to their adaptation to similar environments. On the left, from top to bottom: a shark (cartilaginous fish); an ichthyosaur (marine reptile); and a porpoise (marine mammal). On the right: a spurge plant and a cactus.

When some of these had attained a mammalian level of organization, certain of their members exploited the rich environment afforded by the seas. They "became" whales and porpoises, acquiring a fishlike body with flippers very closely resembling the fins of fishes. Yet there is no going back to exactly what went before. Whales are still mammals and not fishes, as can be easily demonstrated from even a superficial study of their anatomy (bone structure, respiratory and circulatory systems, etc.). They have had to modify already existing mammalian structures to become what they are. The reptiles, in their time, also developed marine-going lineages, and some of these, too, came to resemble fishes outwardly. A streamlined, bullet-shaped body with fins is simply the most effective shape to possess if speed and agility in the water become important.

Now, depending upon the evolutionary distance between the lines developing such similarities of structure, we talk about either **convergence** or **parallelism**. The examples above refer to the former process, since we were discussing very distantly related groups. Parallelism occurs when closely related forms, starting with essentially similar genotypes, and which have become separated, tend to develop side by side in like fashion due to similarities in their environment. Many parallel lines can be demonstrated from the fossil record. Thus within the order of rodents many representative forms (such as mice, squirrels, and beavers) have independently acquired similar (but not identical) constructions in the jaw mechanism related to their mode of feeding by gnawing. In parallelism there exists an implication of concurrent development which tends to keep distinct but closely related lineages different, without becoming notably less or more so through time. In convergence we are dealing with a gradual coming closer (at least outwardly) of two lineages which started very far apart. In both cases adaptation to similar environments is the key factor.

In this connection it might be meaningful to introduce the terms **homologous** and **analogous.** In the previously mentioned wing example, these structures in birds, and in flying reptiles, can be called homologous to each other since both were derived from the same basic pattern, namely the vertebrate forelimb. However, the wing of insects is merely analogous to either one, since it developed from a totally different plan of body organization. The pectoral fins of fishes and our arms are homologous—so are the front flippers of seals and the wings of bats. Homology demonstrates clearly the irrevocability of evolution. Evolution starts with a basic pattern, modifies it, and adapts it to suit different needs—but a close study will always reveal, not only the essential similarity, but also the historical changes in its progressive chronological development. Functionally whale flipper and fish fin are alike, but inspection of the internal make-up will clearly demonstrate the intermediate land vertebrate stage in the case of the seagoing mammal.

Examples of convergence and parallelism can be found in the plant as well as the animal kingdom. Just to mention one, the American deserts abound in many species of **cactus.** The South African arid wastes are also dotted with plants adapted to this stringent environment—only they are not species of cacti but rather belong to an unrelated group, the **spurge** plants. Outwardly it is difficult to tell one from the other, but there is no doubt that they represent quite distinct lineages.

Convergence and parallelism create problems when trying to classify groups of animals in true relation to their evolutionary history, since apparent resemblances can be very misleading.

An even bigger problem in modern classification is the existence of many intermediate forms such as would only be expected if evolution has occurred. Since we have accepted the continuous nature of evolution, we must at the same time realize that classification becomes quite artificial in many ways. Different assemblages are bound to grade one into the other, and arbitrary division lines have to be drawn. As we get to know

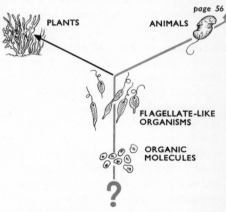

Phylogenetic Tree No. 1 shows life's oldest crossroads—where plants and animals separated into two independent branches. The red line on this and succeeding phylogenetic trees traces man's ancestry. A black line ending in an arrowhead pointing to a drawing indicates that this lineage has continued up to present-day forms of life. Where there is no arrowhead means that here no further development has taken place, that particular evolutionary line having ended in extinction. A number beside an arrowhead indicates that the phyletic continuation of the group is given on a new chart on the page to which the number corresponds.

The Australian duck-billed platypus—a mammal that still retains many reptilian features.

more and more intermediate forms bridging the gap from one group to another, we run into trouble in terms of where exactly to put such "links".

Thus the remarkable Australian **platypus** is counted as a mammal because it has fur, is warm-blooded, and has skin glands that secrete milk, but it lays eggs and in many other respects resembles a reptile. The explanation is that it represents the level of organization common to the very early mammals that developed from certain reptiles. It is really a mammal-like reptile more than a true mammal in the sense that we see mammals represented around us today.

On the dividing line between the plant and animal kingdoms live the **flagellates** —one-celled creatures about which it is impossible to say with certainty whether they are plants or animals. Many of them make their own food like plants—yet they move like animals. In a way they can be considered examples of life's most ancient crossroads from which one line went on to differentiate into the imposing array of algae, mosses, ferns, evergreens, and flowering plants we now group together as the plant kingdom in broad opposition to the other lineage which has yielded all animal life, including ourselves.

LIFE'S BEGINNINGS

"And the earth was without form and void."

These words were written almost three thousand years ago when an unknown Jew recorded the ancient legends of his people concerning the creation of the world, and nobody has since been able to form a sentence that illustrates more simply and precisely the gloom that must have dominated the lifeless beginnings of our globe—the naked mountains and silent deserts, the endless expanse of dead sea, and the unreal silence of the hot, heavy atmosphere.

We do not know how it happened that the barren planet managed to clothe itself with a mantle of teeming life. Its origin is lost in the dim mists of Pre-Cambrian times and can perhaps never be established with certainty. But we can nevertheless draw certain conclusions from our knowledge of present-day life processes and the findings of astronomy, geology, and chemistry concerning natural conditions approximately two billion years ago, when physico-chemical forces began to convert the dead matter of the globe into living mechanisms.

To define life is even more difficult than to define forms of energy such as gravity and radioactivity. We know that it is different from inanimate matter, and we understand some of the essential processes involved in this difference. However, we really are in no position to put our finger on the exact change that occurred when non-living molecules became living entities; that is to say, when they became self-reproducing and were able to use other compounds in their environment for energy.

The chief component of cells today is

The barren earth

protoplasm—a tough jellylike substance whose main elements are carbon, hydrogen, oxygen, and nitrogen. In living matter these elements are combined into molecules of water (about 75%), proteins (about 17%), fats (about 3%), and carbohydrates (about 1%), with various salts (such as sodium and potassium compounds) and traces of relatively rare elements (manganese, copper, zinc, and others) making up the balance. Now it is very interesting to note that at the level of atoms there is no difference between the organism and its inanimate environment. Both are composed of the same elements. It is not until we reach the level of large molecules that we find a difference between living and non-living matter. Proteins, fats, carbohydrates, and other organic compounds are found only in living systems or as a result of their past activity (for example, in coal, oil, or decaying matter). The phenomenon we call life, therefore, is associated with the activity of chemical molecules of large size and complexity.

All living systems are capable of reproduction (in one form or another), and they are all characterized by ceaseless activity which can be maintained only by a continuous expenditure of energy. The organism depends upon its environment for the supply of chemical compounds used in the production of new protoplasm (during growth) and as sources of the energy needed to remain active. The various chemical processes occurring within the organisms are collectively known as **metabolism.** Animals take in food and oxygen, which are partly used to build up the body and partly to meet the energy requirements of the living substance they are composed of. The food, however, cannot just be in the form of simple elements—it must be organic (i.e., composed of complex carbon compounds which are, or have been, living and therefore must be derived from plants or other animals). Green plants, on the other hand, can themselves build up an organic compound—glucose—from inorganic molecules, namely carbon dioxide and water. With glucose as a starting point, plants are able to synthesize other carbohydrates as well as fats and proteins. Carbon dioxide is obtained from the atmosphere, water from the soil, and the energy from sunlight. An additional substance, **chlorophyll,** which is the compound responsible for the green colour of plants, is also necessary. In some way, as yet unknown, chlorophyll is able to convert the energy of light into the chemical energy used to synthesize glucose from carbon dioxide and water. This synthesis, which is finally dependent on light, is known as **photosynthesis.** In this process of glucose formation oxygen is given off. Animals use this free oxygen in their metabolic processes when they assimilate the carbon compounds they have obtained from plants. (Even if they are flesh eaters, they are essentially dependent on plant food since the animals they feed on are herbivores.) Animal metabolism involves an oxidation of these organic compounds to carbon dioxide and water which are returned to the environment. Plants then use these substances to synthesize glucose once again. The parts of this **carbon cycle,** as it is called, are so well balanced that the concentration of carbon dioxide and oxygen in the atmosphere remains constant.

Today a single living cell may appear simple in relation to a whole complex organism, but life in its beginnings al-

Centuries of unceasing rain produced the earth's seas, rivers, and lakes.

most two billion years ago must have been far simpler than any cell we know today. The development from lifelessness to life must have extended over an immeasurable space of time and must have taken place gradually and almost imperceptibly. The first living units must have been difficult to recognize, since they probably were still very close to inanimate chemical systems. The viruses of today probably resemble the first forms of life in that, from a biological viewpoint, these highly specialized parasitic forms belong to the borderland between the living and the non-living. Whether viruses are really primitive or whether they are "degenerate" forms is debatable—but they can be taken as a model of what the properties of some of the first living molecules were like.

According to current theories, the present stage of our universe began about 5000 million years ago. With a tremendous explosion the universe flew apart at that time (Time O). Matter was in the form of elementary particles such as electrons, protons, and neutrons. Thirty minutes later these particles had combined to form the elements helium

and hydrogen—much later the other elements were formed. Our own sun and its planets formed well after the explosion, about 4000 million years ago.

When the solidification of the Earth's crust had advanced so far that the surface temperature of the rocks fell below the boiling point of water, the tremendous banks of clouds, which until then had swathed the globe in eternal night, condensed. Rain began to pour down, gushing like torrential mountain streams over the hills and filling up the valleys and depressions. It most likely rained without ceasing for millennia before the Earth's and the atmosphere's water supply became stabilized. And by the time this equilibrium was established the greater part of the surface of our globe was covered by sea.

The rivers had washed great quantities of earth-dust from the land out into the newly formed oceans, and much points to the fact that we must look for life's origins in that very mud which flowed into the lukewarm surface water of the Pre-Cambrian seas.

For in those times chemical and physical conditions in and above the Earth's crust were quite different from what we know today—and only under these strikingly unusual circumstances can we imagine spontaneous generation to have taken place. By the end of the nineteenth century biologists had come to the conclusion that the spontaneous origin of life was to be excluded in our present world. All life springs into being from already existing living matter, and it is now thought that spontaneous generation occurred possibly only once—namely at the very inception of life.

Conditions consistent with life arose perhaps about 3000 million years ago. At that time the earth's atmosphere contained essentially no free oxygen; all the oxygen was combined as water or oxides. However, there were present large amounts of ammonia (NH_3), methane (CH_4), water vapor (H_2O), and hydrogen (H_2). According to one hypothesis, the prevailing conditions led to the formation of numerous organic compounds until the oceans became a soup of complex carbon molecules.

Recently it has been possible to demonstrate experimentally that the synthesis of organic compounds is, after all, possible without the agency of living systems. Amino acids, which are important building blocks in the formation of complex protein substances, have been produced in the laboratory by exposing the very gases mentioned before as being common at the supposed time of the origin of life to electric discharges. These last can be thought of as taking the place of the violent electric storms that the primeval earth was subjected to frequently. In other words, organic compounds could have been produced under the conditions postulated to have existed many millions of years ago.

The next step would be the formation of a protein molecule, or group of molecules, with very special properties. It is felt that some chance association of organic molecules resulted in a structure that had the ability to form others of its own kind. This point, of course, marks the beginning of life. The best comparison we have for this first living matter is the gene. Genes are able to make copies of themselves from chemical substances present in the cell. The first organisms, too, were able to mould other organic molecules into their own forms. An aggregation of such free "genes", with the ability to undergo heritable changes (mutations), would result in an organism similar in many ways to the present-day submicroscopic viruses.

These first living organisms, having arisen in a sea of organic molecules and in contact with an atmosphere free of oxygen, presumably obtained energy by the **fermentation** of certain of these organic substances. Fermentation is a rather wasteful process of obtaining energy that can take place in the absence of oxygen—a method still utilized by certain bacteria. Such a manner of living could go on only as long as the organic substances accumulated in the past lasted. Eventually some forms must have become capable of photosynthesis—that is, of manufacturing some of their own complex organic molecules.

Competition for the required organic substances increased as more and more of the available supply was exhausted. Evolution took place in the direction of an increasing ability to synthesize food from only carbon dioxide, water, and inorganic salts. When this point was reached, so was a corresponding degree of liberation from the environment, and the great diversity of organic forms that the earth has known was well on the way.

The "inventors" of chlorophyll became the progenitors of the green plants. These in a way can be said to have paid for their "ingenuity" by being tied down to a life of permanent immobility. Animals have retained primeval life's dependency on organic nutrition and therefore must seek out their food, for which reason they were "obliged" to develop mobility and sense organs.

Three quarters of the saga of Life is a book with almost completely blank pages.

Pre-Cambrian times lasted well over 2,500 million years, with life originating probably about 2,000 million years ago, somewhere within the first half of this enormously long span. Tremendous deposits all over the Earth are considered to have been formed during these primeval times, but the mile-thick layers tell us almost nothing about the oldest forms of life on our globe.

In North American Pre-Cambrian formations there have been identified—although with some doubt—a few tracks made by **wormlike creature** a few fossil fragments from Australia and America have been dubiously presented as being remains of primitive **arthropods;** impressions in a sandstone rock in Sweden are believed to have originated from a Pre-Cambrian

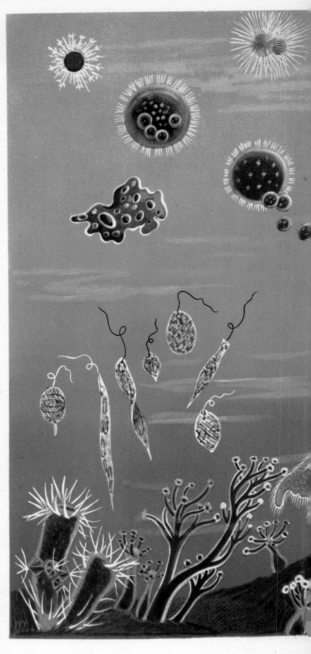

A scientific reconstruction of some of life's oldest representatives probably populating the Pre-Cambrian oceans. On the bottom can be seen some of the first sponges and polyps and to the far right

group of primitive algae. On the left above the ⟨sp⟩onges some flagellates are swimming with an ⟨am⟩oeba directly above them. At the top right are ⟨tw⟩o spherical flagellate colonies surrounded by one-⟨cel⟩led radiolarians. On the right are two long-tenta-cled jellyfish, a segmented worm, and, at the top, two primitive flatworms. For the sake of clarity the animals have not been drawn to scale. For instance, both the flagellates and radiolarians are in reality microscopic creatures.

jellyfish; elsewhere a traces few of spongelike organisms and what are believed to be one-celled radiolarians have been found. Recently flagellates have tentatively been identified from Pre-Cambrian strata. The oldest fossils surely recognized are at least 1,000 million years old. They are simple water plants, algae, primitive enough to be sure, and yet already several strides along the road of evolution.

And that is about all.

The almost complete lack of tangible evidence of organic life in Pre-Cambrian formations can to a certain extent be put down to their tremendous age; they are almost all greatly transformed, and in general the position of the strata has been violently disturbed.

The main reason that the fossils discovered do not give any true picture of the Pre-Cambrian life is that the first organisms were in all probability much smaller and simpler even than our present-day amoeba. As mentioned before, most biologists think that they had the size and characteristics of genes. A fossil gene would be rather difficult to find and study.

By the beginning of the next geological period, the Cambrian, 500 million years ago, the sea was already teeming with living creatures which must have had a very long period of evolution behind them. The invertebrate animal phyla are all represented in Cambrian deposits and must have come into existence far back in the Pre-Cambrian.

That all these main phylogenetic branches cannot be documented below the Cambrian simply means that the Pre-Cambrian animals had still not developed shells and other hard parts which could be preserved as fossils.

In the course of the Pre-Cambrian the first primeval life systems developed into cells and thence further to multicellular animals and plants.

It was a long road. The distance from the living organic molecule to the unicellular organism was probably greater than the span from a unicellular form to man. The very nature of the cumulative process that is evolution implies an effect of acceleration. Early stages were aeon-long and slow beyond imagination. They built a basis on which, finally, more rapid evolution occurred.

To judge by living representatives, one-celled animals led a primitive life and reproduced themselves by breaking into two parts. Sometimes two cells would fuse, exchange genetic material, and break apart again. This process is called conjugation, and it can be compared to sexual reproduction since it involves a reshuffling of genes in the resultant "offspring"—just as does the formation and fusion of sperm and ovum to produce the embryo.

Eventually numbers of cells joined together in colonies. Here the functions of life were divided among them by groups. Certain cells specialized in catching food, while others busied themselves with digestion. Some became sex cells and concerned themselves exclusively with propagation; another group took upon itself the task of making the colony mobile and self-governing so

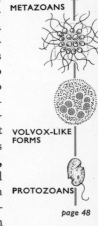

page 61

METAZOANS

VOLVOX-LIKE FORMS

PROTOZOANS

page 48

Phylogenetic Tree No. 2

that it no longer had to float helplessly with the ocean currents but became somewhat independent in its movements.

By means of such steadily increasing specialization some of the colonies of unicellular forms gradually developed into multicellular animals. These were, to begin with, probably no more than gelatinous spheres with an internal cavity and an opening which served both as mouth and anus.

A living example of the transition from the unicellular to multicellular level of organization is *Volvox*. This is a colonial flagellate with some cells specialized for locomotion, some for nutrition, and a very special set for reproduction. It might be said that with a form like *Volvox* **death** entered the world. For a one-celled organism does not die in the accepted sense. If reproduction only involves a simple splitting in two, then there is nothing left of what has gone before. *Volvox* sends forth its daughter colonies to grow and reproduce in turn, while it itself dies. Specialization at the cellular level means that the individual has subjected itself to the inexorable laws of all subsequent life: to be born, to grow, and to die.

The nervous system and the sense organs must have come into being during Pre-Cambrian times. Protoplasm itself is sensitive to chemical stimuli as well as to light—both an amoeba and the eyeless earthworm can react to chemical differences and distinguish between light and darkness. An eye as such, developed when cells particularly sensitive to light gathered together in local groups. The same process must have occurred in the development of special organs for smelling, tasting, and hearing. Specialized cells came into existence for the integration of all the various stimuli received from the environment. These **nerve cells** became concentrated into a **nerve cord** (located along the region of the back in **chordates**). The front portion of this cord, near the mouth and particularly concerned with sense organs involved in the collection of food, grew in size and eventually became the **brain.**

The first animals with a digestive cavity of sorts were jellyfishes and polyps (the **coelenterates**). Ancestral **flatworms** probably developed the first distinct nervous system, and before the end of the Pre-Cambrian a small but very important little animal must have turned up. From it are descended the **echinoderms** (starfishes, sea urchins, etc.), but it is also believed to have had other more "important" descendants; for, in all probability, another of its lineages was that of the chordates—the group to which all **vertebrates,** including ourselves, belong.

All the major phyla then, except the chordates specifically, must have developed during the aeons of time we call the Pre-Cambrian, since, when we enter the Paleozoic Era—with the fossil-rich Cambrian period before us—we find all the main invertebrate groups fully differentiated and, by the end of the Cambrian, represented in teeming abundance throughout the marine waters of those times.

THE PALEOZOIC SEAS

When the Pre-Cambrian came to a close about 500 million years ago, life must already have been in existence for some 1500 million years. But the results were by no means impressive. Compared with the snail-like pace of Pre-Cambrian development, the first 170 million years of the Paleozoic Era, which comprise the **Cambrian, Ordovician,** and **Silurian** periods, can'be regarded as a veritable explosion.

The Cambrian period lasted approximately 75 million years, the Ordovician about 65 million, and the Silurian around 30 million years.

Geologic evidence shows that around the middle of the Cambrian period the oceans began to rise and gradually invaded much of the land, forming shallow inland seas over many of the continents. At the beginning of the Cambrian period the continents probably covered roughly the some area as today, but as it progressed, and later in the course of the Ordovician, perhaps one half of this total land area became submerged. The land was reduced to groups of very large islands intersected by arms of the sea.

The restricted climatic belts of the present day did not appear until much later in the history of the earth—and the climate was mild (possibly subtropical to tropical) over most of the globe. The weather may have changed character now and again, but its effects were not felt below the surface of the sea. During the Ordovician period coral reefs stretched in an unbroken line from Greenland to the Antarctic.

The first half of the Paleozoic Era can be called the **Age of the Invertebrates.**

The scene of development was in the water. The land was completely barren, but in the sea life flourished and spread from pole to pole.

A very important event was the appearance of armour on the bodies of animals. As the density of the population in the oceans increased, competition became accentuated and made it necessary for organisms to develop both means of defence and means of inflicting death. The perpetual race between weapons of attack and mechanisms for protection of an elaborate nature started in the Cambrian sea.

At the beginning of the Cambrian period we already meet the entire range of invertebrates, from primitive **sponges** to highly developed **arthropods,** the **trilobites.**

Spongelike organisms built colossal reefs in many parts of the world, but they became extinct for unknown reasons before the Cambrian had reached its halfway mark. Beautiful **glass sponges** (with internal supports made of silica) were also to be found in many places.

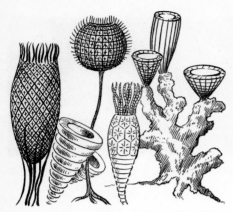

Sponges and spongelike organisms of the Paleo-zoic Sea. They look like plants but are really among the most primitive of multicellular animals.

The sponges are the most primitive of all multicellular animals and have survived almost unaltered from the Cambrian to the present day. Sponges are believed to be an evolutionary side line which has never given rise directly to any of the other more complex multicellular forms, such as coelenterates, flatworms, etc. They are sedentary animals when adult, but in their larval (or very early) stages they resemble mobile flagellate colonies. In their adaptation to an attached life on the bottom of the ocean they have never developed muscles, nerves, or other sense organs. Sponges show cellular differentiation, but there is no cellular co-operation to form special tissues and organs. They are living filters—water streams in through pores placed all through the walls of the body, which is usually vase shaped or cylindrical, and is expelled by way of a larger common opening at one end. The water brings with it microscopic food particles that are extracted and digested by specialized cells. However, there is no common digestive cavity.

Many kinds of worms were probably widely distributed, since their tracks and casts of their burrows are common in Cambrian sandstone formations. One of these of which we have a good impression, *Aysheaia,* resembles a living form that is regarded as intermediate in organization between **segmented worms (annelids)** and arthropods. *Aysheaia* probably stood close to the common ancestor of these two phyla, which must have started to diverge during Pre-Cambrian times.

In the Cambrian numerous kinds of invertebrates grew protective shells, among them the **molluscs.** These had become differentiated by this time into three groups of diverse life habits. There were the relatively passive bottom-dwelling filter feeders, which developed into the **pelecypods** (or bivalves—e.g., clams), the crawling carnivorous or herbivorous **gastropods** (or snails), and the swimming predatory **cephalopods** (nautiloids, octopi, squids, etc.). Cambrian gastropods were represented mainly by uncoiled cap-shaped forms and flatly coiled types—the characteristic high snail shell we know did not become common until later. Pelecypods do not appear in the fossil record until the next period, the Ordovician. However, primitive **nautiloids**—the ancestral lineage of all the cephalopods—are present by the end of the Cambrian, although their period of dominance was not yet at hand.

The **echinoderms** were relatively rare during the Cambrian. Among them the most common types were stemmed forms —that is, they had a stalk by means of which they attached themselves to the bottom. Most of these had a saclike body surrounded by calcified plates and free armlike appendages. There were **edrio-**

Scene on the bottom of the Cambrian Sea. To the left are eocrinoids, very primitive sea lilies. On the right are three trilobites in front of a group of beautiful glass sponges. In the foreground creeps the primitive arthropod *Aysheaia,* and behind it lie brachiopods and Cambrian snails.

asteroids (possibly the ancestors of the starfishes or **asteroids**), **eocrinoids** (primitive sea lilies or **crinoids**), and **carpoids.** The last had curiously flattened shapes, mostly without appendages, with the stem modified in the form of a short tail-like structure. They probably lived by lying on the bottom and in many ways resembled nothing so much as some of the earliest vertebrates—the **ostracoderms**—which we shall discuss later.

One of the most successful of the Paleozoic phyla were the **lamp shells,** or **brachiopods.** These have two shells like clams, except that the shells lie above and below the body instead of on the right and left sides. They account for a large percentage of all Cambrian fossils. From the beginning of the

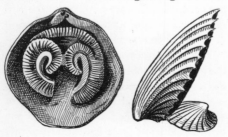

A brachiopod. Notice its ciliated and coiled appendages for feeding.

Cambrian there were two main types of brachiopods present. Most of the earliest forms had shells that were made of chitin and held together only by rather weak muscles—these are the **inarticulate** brachiopods—among which a living genus, *Lingula,* is a practically unchanged form that dates back to the Lower Cambrian. The other line, although equally old, did not become important until toward the end of the Cambrian. These are the **articulate** brachiopods, with heavy calcareous shells held together by a powerful hinge joint. Both lineages are still represented in present-day oceans, and a study of the living animals has revealed many interesting features. The bottom shell is attached to the ground or some other hard object by means of a sturdy stalk. Their internal anatomy is relatively complex; they have a nervous as well as a circulatory system and a complete digestive tube. They feed on microscopic particles which are drawn to the interior of the slightly open valves by water currents created by movements of hairlike structures, called cilia, located on long coiled appendages situated near the mouth.

One of the earliest offshoots of the arthropods were the trilobites. They were the rulers of the early Paleozoic seas, at least in terms of numbers and variety of species. In contrast to most of the other invertebrates then around they were active walking and swimming forms. Trilobites remained very successful until the end of the Ordovician when they began to taper off, to become extinct by the end of the Paleozoic Era. Many were good swimmers; others crawled among the stones and waving seaweed forests on the bottom of the sea, while grubbing for food in the mud. They never became very big. The giant of Cambrian trilobites was *Paradoxides,* about thirty inches long. Some trilobites had large, compound, faceted eyes, but others—like *Agnostus,* for instance—appear to have been completely blind. *Agnostus* probably lived buried in the soft mud of the ocean bottom and was about the size of a pea.

The Cambrian period was succeeded by the Ordovician, and while the oceans slowly invaded more and more of the continents, life celebrated new triumphs of variety in the aggressive sea.

The trilobites were the rulers of the Cambrian Sea. The largest of them, the thirty-inch *Paradoxides,* was one of the giants of its time.

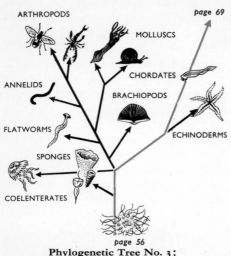

ARTHROPODS

page 69

MOLLUSCS

CHORDATES

ANNELIDS

BRACHIOPODS

FLATWORMS

ECHINODERMS

SPONGES

COELENTERATES

page 56

Phylogenetic Tree No. 3:
Invertebrate Animals

The first true clams (pelecypods) made their appearance, and together with them their most deadly enemy, the starfishes (asteroids), an echinoderm lineage whose representatives are unattached and can move freely. The "old-fashioned" attached types were still around, and there were even some additions to these: the sea lilies (crinoids) and two other sessile groups called **cystoids** and **blastoids.**

During the Ordovician the oldest known coral reefs spread from pole to pole. The corals are colonial coelenterates that live within complicated cal-

Graptolites.

careous structures which they secrete. Millions upon millions of these creatures together build up the tremendous formation that is a coral reef.

Another group of colonial organisms, the "moss animals" (**Bryozoa**) are first recorded from the Ordovician. They also secrete calcareous encasements but are quite distinct anatomically from the corals. They are on about the same level of organization as brachiopods, and their colonial edifices, looking like weirdly branching antlers, are often found fossilized. Many still live today, mostly in marine environments.

Both the brachiopods and the gastropods (snails) developed innumerable species. The majority of coiled snail shells were relatively low, but by now there was also a good proportion with high, beautifully spiralled shells. The echinoderms, as mentioned before, were in addition to the originally Cambrian forms, also represented by graceful sea lilies which formed weaving, animated forests on the bottom of the sea. There were also present the first identifiable sea urchins, sea cucumbers, and brittle stars.

The trilobites were at their height in numbers and variety of species, but none of them were nearly as impressive as some of the shelled cephalopods—the nautiloids which were beginning an "explosive" radiation at that time. These active predators were excellent swimmers. Some attained lengths of over fifteen feet and were thus the mightiest creatures of the early Paleozoic seas. Some of the trilobites developed grotesque weapons of defense against these aggressive giants, and others learned to roll themselves up like present-day pill bugs or sow bugs (also arthropods—but of a different lineage) in order to protect

Here is a giant nautiloid catching a trilobite in the Ordovician Sea. Around its long, torpedolike shell swarm sea scorpions. At the top sails a colony of graptolites with their peculiar swim bladder. On the bottom, brachiopods, snails, and starfish. On the right, next to the giant snail and the yellow, vase-shaped sponges, a few sea lilies. On the left, a carpoid lying on the bottom.

their soft undersides. (A parallel development, if you will, that took place long after the trilobites became extinct.)

The tremendous expansion of the nautiloids, however, was not the only striking event during the Ordovician period. The **graptolites** were also entering upon a period of rapid diversification and distribution. They were small, colonial animals with a chitinous outer covering in the shape of tubes or cups arranged in regular patterns along branches. The first ones appeared in the lowermost Ordovician, and in the course of that period they spread over the whole globe in such vast quantities that in certain places they overshadow all other types of fossils now found. They were real globe-trotters in their distribution. Their colonies were carried by the drift of ocean currents to every corner of the earth. Many of them developed an odd-looking swim-bladder type of arrangement for floating purposes. The graptolites are usually placed into a separate phylum, but modern research and very detailed electronmicroscopic study has indicated that they should be placed, together with polyps, jellyfishes, and corals, into the coelenterate phylum. There is also some evidence that would relate graptolites to some of the very primitive chordates that are still living (such as the **tunicates** or sea squirts). In either case, it is highly probable that graptolites do not represent a distinct phylum. If they did, theirs would be the only such major grouping to have become extinct. All the phyla that we find from the Cambrian on are still with us today.

When the Ordovician period was gradually succeeded by the Silurian, the invertebrates were still reigning supreme. A few lines flourished; some "decayed"— their void being taken up by others.

The graptolites were beginning their decline and had already become rare in some places. Trilobites were still common but had long since passed their zenith of diversity.

The corals, on the other hand, began to branch out into great variety of species, and the sea lilies, too, really "exploded" into a great many different forms. Many of the other primitive attached echinoderms were either extinct by now or declining rapidly in numbers—although the blastoids were just beginning their period of increased speciation. During the Silurian the brachiopods also showed extraordinary powers of differentiation—especially the articulate line. Apart from the flat, broad forms, highly arched, almost spherical types appeared whose upper shell had a pointed overhanging margin. What the significance of many of these shell forms and their odd ornamentation might have been in terms of adapation to a particular way of life is difficult to surmise. Perhaps there was a relationship between the various depths of the ocean at which these brachiopods lived and the type of shell best suited to maintain the animal efficiently at various levels.

We have a much better explanation for the development of the peculiarly long, torpedo-shaped or variously-coiled shell that characterized the early cephalopods —the nautiloids. These were not bottom-dwellers and, being swimmers, would have been limited to a light delicate shell affording little protection had they not hit on another solution. By installing air-filled, buoyant chambers, separated by walls and connected to the body by a long inner tube, the cephalopods were

A sea scorpion whips through the Silurian Sea. In front of it a nautiloid with a spiralled shell. On the far right, one of the first primitive fish.

able to eat their cake (in peace, due to the protection of a thick shell) and have it too (in the sense of still being light enough to be excellent swimmers). Silurian nautiloids continued the tremendous expansion of their group which had commenced in earnest during the Ordovician. However, by the end of the Silurian their numbers had already dropped and have continued to do so at a fairly even rate—the group ending in just a few modern representatives. As the nautiloids declined, they were replaced by the **ammonoids,** one of their offshoots during late Silurian times. The latter, mostly coiled forms with more complicated shell partitions than their forebears, reached their peak in the Mesozoic oceans but became extinct at the end of that era.

The arthropods had by now developed a most impressive lineage—that of the **eurypterids** or sea scorpions. Their remains are found in deposits ranging from the Ordovician to the end of the Paleozoic era—but the Silurian period seems to have been their time of greatest abundance. Many were larger than a man—some as long as nine feet. Their streamlined body and oar-shaped hindmost appendages must have made them excellent swimmers. They had long clawed forelimbs attached to the head. Some authorities think they swam on their backs and lived in shallow, semi-enclosed brackish water lagoons, rather than in the open sea inhabited by the other invertebrates of the time.

While the cephalopods and the eurypterids were developing giant types, one of life's greatest innovations was in the process of being unswathed.

The "lords of creation"—the vertebrates—were on their way!

65

THE FIRST FISHES AND THEIR DESCENDANTS

The first vertebrates, jawless fishlike forms called **ostracoderms,** probably developed in shallow rivers and inland lakes. Their proficiency at swimming points towards their having evolved in running water, and the oldest traces are found in Ordovician and Silurian deposits which have been interpreted by most authorities as being of fresh-water origin. It must have been at a later date that they spread to the oceans. (This of course does not exclude the possibility that the early stem chordates that gave rise to these presumably fresh-water vertebrates were marine creatures.)

We do not know what the progenitor of the first known vertebrates looked like, but along the coasts of America and Europe there still lives today a semitransparent little creature that perhaps gives an indication of the appearance of our earliest forebears. This is the **lancelet,** known as *Amphioxus*. Shaped like a willow leaf, this little animal looks really more like a worm than a fish and is, at first sight, a rather unimpressive creature.

Section through a lancelet. The black notochord is the early equivalent of the spinal column of vertebrates.

The lancelet has neither head, jaws, nor well-defined sense organs, and its colourless blood is pumped round the body by pulsating vessels, for it has no heart either.

Nevertheless, the lancelet is a *true* chordate. Down the entire length of its body runs a "back-string", or **notochord,** which represents the precursor of the backbone or spinal column. Above the notochord is a hollow nerve cord, and below it is a simple digestive tube, the front part of which is pierced by gill slits. Muscles are arranged in clearly marked segments all along both sides of the notochord. All these features agree remarkably with our conception of what an early generalized vertebrate forebear should look like. *Amphioxus* has one marked specialization though. It is supplied with a tremendous number of gills (many more than are characteristic of later vertebrates) arranged in a long series down either side of the front portion of the body. These not only serve to extract oxygen from the water but also aid the animal in feeding by functioning as a sort of sieve to strain food from the debris of the ocean floor.

The early vertebrates underwent a tremendous period of expansion in the latter half of the Paleozoic Era, starting with the **Devonian** (of 50 million years duration), and later during the **Carbonif-**

Some of the first vertebrates: four ostracoderms (jawless) and one placoderm (with jaws). Clockwise beginning at the far right: *Climatius,* the oldest known fish with jaws; *Pterolepis; Hemicyclaspis; Cephalaspis; Pteraspis.*

erous (60 million years) and the **Permian** (30 million years) periods.

The very first vertebrates, the ostracoderms, were jawless and mostly fairly slow, bottom-dwelling types. Charac-

One of the placoderms, *Coccosteus,* an arthrodire —or "joint neck". Two ostracoderms, *Pteraspis,* in background.

teristically they were covered with plates of heavy calcareous armour. The mouth was usually a round suckerlike opening near the bottom of the head end of the animal.

During the transition from the Silurian to the Devonian, primitive fishlike forms were the only representatives of the vertebrates in the Paleozoic lakes and oceans. Among the ostracoderms the most important groups were the **cephalaspids** and the **pteraspids,** both of which had the head and front of the body encased in solid bony armour plating. The cephalaspids were flat bottom dwellers with a broadly rounded head shield, while the pteraspids were slim, with the narrow rear part of the body sticking out of a strangely domed and forwardly elongated cuirass. A third group was that of the **anaspids;** their bodies had no jointed head or body armour—instead they were covered with small grainlike

Several members of the genus *Bothriolepis*. These were curiously-shaped placoderms, called antiarchs, whose pectoral appendages were jointed and could be moved just like arms. At bottom left lie the remains of a dead antiarch's armour; this is how we find this fish today as a fossil.

scales. In some of the anaspids there was a marked reduction of even this modified armour, and it is possible that the surviving **lampreys** and **hagfishes** (which are grouped together with the ostracoderms into the **Agnatha** or jawless fishes) are descended from them. The lamprey, although having become a parasitic form in the course of its evolution, shows many close resemblances to the first jawless vertebrates.

The earliest fishlike vertebrates with jaws—the **placoderms**—had appeared by the end of the Silurian period. All the placoderms had—in addition to lower mandibles—upper jaws that were firmly attached to the skull. Behind the jaws there was a full gill slit, and all of these early jawed fishes had paired fins of a variable number. The first represented group among them was that of the

acanthodians, or "spiny sharks" (not true sharks though). Their body was covered with diamond-shaped, heavy scales, and in front of each back fin rose a sharp, pointed spine. The early acanthodians have characteristics which point both towards the cartilaginous fishes, or sharks, as well as the "bony fishes", and they are possibly close to the direct progenitors of both these two groups of higher fishes—the **Chondrichthyes** and the **Osteichthyes** respectively.

The fishes acquired jaws when the mouth grew in size, so to speak, and incorporated the frontmost gill arch. During a later stage of evolutionary development the next branchial arch (the **hyoid** arch), was taken in, too, to serve as a prop between brain case and jaws. The eustachian tube and middle-ear cavity in amphibians, reptiles, and mammals is what is left of the first gill slit behind the jaws. One of the middle-ear bones, the stapes, which serves to conduct sound vibrations from the ear membrane to the inner ear, is actually homologous to the upper part of the hyoid arch in fishes.

In the seas and lakes of the Devonian period there lived other groups of placoderms, related to the acanthodians. There were the **arthrodires** or "joint-necks", and the curious **antiarchs**. The arthrodires were quite small initially but later developed giant forms up to thirty feet long—rapacious, predatory fishes with powerful jaws and sturdy, toothlike bony blades in their mouths. The antiarchs were rather odd looking creatures. The front part of the body was enclosed in a boxlike protective armour, and they had paired, armoured front fins that were jointed in several places along their length. These were articulated to the body and could be moved almost like arms. Their use is debatable, but they may have enabled the antiarchs to crawl around on the bottom.

The placoderms, as a group, became extinct with the demise of the acanthodians at the end of the Permian, with all their other representatives having already died out by the end of the Devonian. They were replaced in the oceans of the world by the Osteichthyes (bony fishes) and the Chondrichthyes (cartilaginous fishes), both of which appear by the beginning of the Devonian and both of which are believed to have sprung from a placoderm ancestry. At one time it was felt that the cartilaginous fishes, or sharks, were more primitive than the bony fishes—but this is not the case. Both are independent lineages derived at approximately the same time.

The bony fishes, from their very be-

ginning, can be divided into three main groups: the **Actinopterygii**, or ray-finned fishes, which include the ancestors of the present-day bony fishes, the **Crossopterygii**, or "lobe fins", and the **Dipnoi**, or lungfishes.

Certain of the lobe fins gave rise to a new class of land-going vertebrates, the amphibians, while the ray-finned fishes developed in a really explosive manner, but only as far as aquatic environments are concerned. The actinopterygians can be conveniently arranged into three groupings, each one representing a successively "higher" level of organization. The **chondrosteans** were the primitive ray-finned fishes that occurred from the Devonian to the Permian, with a few forms (such as the **sturgeon**) surviving into the Recent. They were replaced by the **holosteans** (Triassic through Cretaceous), with a few survivors, such as the **gar,** still present today. The most advanced grouping are the **teleosts** which have a completely ossified vertebral column (as contrasted to a partly

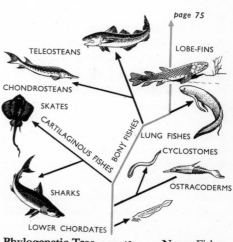

page 75

TELEOSTEANS   LOBE-FINS

CHONDROSTEANS

SKATES

CARTILAGINOUS FISHES   BONY FISHES

LUNG FISHES

CYCLOSTOMES

SHARKS   OSTRACODERMS

LOWER CHORDATES

Phylogenetic Tree *page 62*   **No. 4: Fishes**

69

cartilaginous one in their forerunners). Also, the heavy rhombic (called **ganoid**) scales characteristic of the earlier two groups have given place to thin, rounded scales. Often the chondrosteans and holosteans are collectively referred to as ganoids. The skull, too, has undergone changes, particularly in the cheek and jaw region, leading to a more efficient feeding mechanism. The teleosts started to become important about sixty million years ago (during the Cretaceous) and have since that time filled the lakes, rivers, and oceans of the world. Objectively speaking, the success of the teleosts, in terms of numbers of genera and species, probably exceeds that of the mammals.

However, we have gone far ahead in our story. To get an idea of the historical events that led to the evolution of mammals (including ourselves) we have to retrace our steps to the Devonian. For it is somewhere in this period that one of the many aquatic lines of vertebrates by now present became "able to go ashore". Terrestrial existence with its tremendous evolutionary potentialities had become possible.

LIFE GOES ASHORE

Towards the end of the Silurian period the land began to rise again. This was the time of the **Caledonian Revolution,** a period of earth disturbances and of the building in Europe of great mountains of which the Scottish Highlands and the Scandinavian ranges are remnants.

It used to be thought by many scientists (some still do to this day) that during the latter half of the Paleozoic Era and the beginning of the Mesozoic Era there existed (from the Silurian period on) one continuous land mass in the Southern Hemisphere, called **Gondwanaland.** In it were included all the southern continents, that is, South America, Africa, peninsular India, and Australia. This huge southern land mass was thought to have been separated from an equally extensive conjoined land area (Eurasia and North America) by an east-west **Tethys Sea.** However, the findings used as evidence for such a theory can be more simply explained in terms of **disjunctive** distribution. That is to say, rather than imagine tremendously different (as compared with now) continental relationships at various times in the past in order to explain the distribution of certain fossil and living types of animals and plants common only to these supposedly at one time joined areas, it is really more scientific to reason as follows: A formerly universal distribution has been broken up (by extinction and replacement in the northern continents), thus leaving what is called a disjunctive distribution. There is no doubt that all through the history of the Earth land connections between certain continents, such as North America and the Eurasian land mass (the Bering Strait), Eurasia and Africa (the Suez isthmus), and North and South America (the Panama isthmus), have been above and below sea level intermittently, together with a possible past connection between South Asia and Australia. The existence or interruption of these bridges are sufficient to explain the distribution of most fossil and living forms. There is therefore no reason to bring in any additional notions, such as Gondwanaland, for instance. It is simpler to suppose that the continents as we known them today have always been approximately in the same relative positions to each other, rather than indiscriminately to build hypothetical and extensive land connections bridging the Atlantic and Pacific oceans, in order to explain faunal and floral distributions that could have reasonably come about through the make or break of the four connections mentioned before. The absence of geographically linking forms, that sometimes occurs, is due to the random nature of preservation and collecting in general.

But to return to what is actually known to have occurred towards the end of the Silurian—many of the shallow marine incursions that had covered much of the land during early Paleozoic times were by now in retreat, and a lot of continental "acreage" was becoming exposed again. And while the waters retreated, life clung to the newly emerging land.

The Silurian-Devonian transition marks the beginning of the record of land plants. The plants were the first to colonize the land and make it habitable. Simple aquatic forms without leaves, stems, or roots (algae or seaweed, in other words) achieved for the first time vascular stems, leaves, and simple roots —structures developed for life on land and for drawing moisture from the soil. In changing from aquatic to terrestrial habits, the plants developed supporting tissues and a leathery cuticle for protection against drying out. The earliest land plants are mosses and ferns. Competition for sunlight produced taller and taller forms until eventually trees and forests covered much of the earth. Smaller ferns and horsetails formed the undercover, as they do today. Giant tree ferns developed, and there were big, heavily-barked club mosses. Among the most impressive developments in the history of evolution is that of the modest algae which after a thousand million years of life in the sea had progressed no further than to become simple, rootless and leafless seaweed

Aquatic plants begin to clothe the rising land.

but once having established a foothold on land, were able—over a short fifty million years—to clothe the barren mountain ranges and bare deserts of the earth in a luxuriating carpet of teeming vegetation.

The wide open spaces of early Devonian lands, just beginning to be made habitable by primitive land plants, were soon exploited by members of the animal kingdom.

The arthropods were among the first pioneers to develop special lineages adapted to a terrestrial existence. We begin to find primitive **scorpions, millipedes,** and **spiders.** These had all found ways to change their breathing gills, formerly adapted to get oxygen from water, to structures able to obtain this precious element directly from the air. Some molluscs, too, became land living—developing into the pulmonate ("lunged") snails.

By the end of the Devonian myriads of **insects** (also an arthropod assemblage) must have swarmed among the trees of the fern forests. There were primitive wingless types as well as some of the early winged forms. By Carboniferous times some of these had developed giant representatives. There were primitive **dragonflies** with a wingspread of over two feet, **May flies** almost five inches across, and four-inch long **cockroaches.**

But of greatest interest to us, naturally, is the invasion of land by the vertebrates.

The Devonian appears to have been a period marked by seasonal as well as longer periods of drought. The drying up of many lakes and rivers must have had disastrous consequences for the animals that lived in them.

First and foremost, it must have affected those great consumers of oxygen—the fishes. When the level of the water sank, the oxygen content of the water decreased accordingly, and the fishes probably had to supplement the meagre oxygen ration obtained by means of gills, with an additional amount derived directly from the air. From the geological evidence it appears that most Devonian vertebrate faunas were concentrated in fresh water in inland lakes and streams, and it is quite conceivable that the majority of the Devonian fishes had evolved lungs in order to be able to snap up air at the surface of the rather stagnant waters they inhabited. Those lines which radiated out to become seagoing types somewhat later in geologic history had no further use for lungs in the well-oxygenated open ocean, and the swim bladder (an organ used for balance) developed out of the same anatomical structure that had primitively functioned as a lung.

Today we know only two groups of air-breathing fishes. One of them comprises the lungfishes, whose ancestors we find from the Devonian on. Living representatives occur in Australia, South Africa, and South America. That this group was once very widespread is shown from fossil remains from both Europe and North America. The spotty occurrences we find today are a good example of the disjunctive type of distribution discussed previously. The other group of airbreathers includes the earth's most famous conquistadores: the **crossopterygians** or lobe fins.

From thorough study of the skeleton it is possible to establish that the crossopterygians had all the characteristics that we might expect in the ancestors of the **tetrapods**—as the four-legged land vertebrates are called. From the time of

On the shore of a Devonian lake some 350 million years ago. In the shallow water are two primitive lungfishes *(Dipterus)*.

their appearance they evolved in two main directions. One lineage comprises the ancestors of all the tetrapods, but the other became far removed from this "main line" of evolution. This group, the **coelacanths,** became predominantly marine fishes that until very recently were thought to have become extinct at the end of the Mesozoic Era. However, in 1939 a living coelacanth, the famous *Latimeria,* was dredged up off the coast of South Africa. Since then many more have been captured and are now being carefully studied.

The other lobe-finned group, the **rhipidistians,** include forms such as *Eusthenopteron,* which show both in skull and in internal fin structure all the necessary elements from which the amphibian skull and the tetrapod limb could logically be derived. They had internal nostrils, indicating that they possessed lungs, and powerful muscles in their two sets of paired fins.

The reasons for the evolution of the tetrapods can only be surmised, but one rather appealing hypothesis is the following: Limbs initially developed from fins, not so much to further existence on land but rather to enable the lobe fins to crawl to neighboring still filled pools of water when the seasonal drought set in. Thus, ironically, limbs were originally an adaptation to be able to remain in the water. Once able to crawl about, further selection for efficient limbs might have occurred when the now available terrestrial food supply (insects and plants)

73

The lobe fins (*Eusthenopteron*) go ashore.

became important to certain of those early "links" between lobe fins and true tetrapods.

But a more permanent life on land produced other problems apart from breathing and locomotion. Although the latter could present difficulties enough for a creature whom the force of gravity had never previously bothered, the danger of desiccation was to prove an even graver problem.

Life, after all, has sprung from the sea. Protoplasm consists for the greater part of water, and if the moisture content of the body falls below a certain level, all

Latimeria—a surviving member of a specialized side branch of the lobe-finned fishes.

the processes necessary to life simply cease.

For a fish in water moisture naturally involves no problems. But on dry land conditions are completely different. Here control of body-water evaporation is a matter of life and death.

The first amphibians, then, had to adopt measures against desiccation before becoming even halfway independent of a watery environment. Control sufficient to enable tetrapods to live and reproduce themselves wholly on land never did develop at the amphibian level. Such a degree of independence was attained only millions of years later with the appearance of the first reptiles.

By the end of the Devonian period we find the first four-legged vertebrates dragging themselves along on the belly near the edges of the swamps of eastern Greenland. These were the **ichthyostegids**—the first known amphibians. They looked like lobe fins in many ways, but they already possessed that hallmark of the land vertebrate—the tetrapod limb unequivocally developed in all its parts, from its junction to the trunk, down to the endmost five appendages (the fingers and toes).

Luxuriant forest swamps stretched across the land during the Carboniferous period. A damp subtropical climate must have predominated over most of the globe, and the heavy atmosphere must have quivered with moisture beneath the hothouse roof formed by the massive clouds.

Dark and melancholy were these swamp forests. (Their remains have formed thick deposits of coal in many parts of the earth.) To our eyes they would have appeared as a strange sight, like a foreign planet. No gaudy flowers broke the monotonous gloom of the wilderness. Everything was green—an endless, unbroken green. Even the

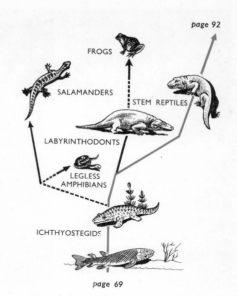

page 92

FROGS

SALAMANDERS

STEM REPTILES

LABYRINTHODONTS

LEGLESS AMPHIBIANS

ICHTHYOSTEGIDS

page 69

Phylogenetic Tree No. 5: Amphibians

trunks of the trees were wrapped in a sheath of dark green leaves.

Giant ferns many feet tall stretched up

The first land vertebrates—the ancestral amphibians called ichthyostegids—on the banks of a swamp in the then subtropical environment of East Greenland.

from the black waters of the swamps. The Carboniferous club mosses included large trees (the living relics are small, fairly common plants consisting of four genera with hundreds of species). There was *Sigillaria,* crowned with odd-looking "tassels", and *Lepidodendron,* a hundred feet and more tall. Twining plants coiled in tangled festoons from tree to tree, and every available spot must have been choked with rampant vegetation.

The oldest amphibians almost certainly spent relatively little of their time on "terra firma". On land they had to drag themselves along on their stomachs as their limbs and vertebral column were as yet too weak structurally to bear the weight of their bodies efficiently. Very early in amphibian evolution, however, the rather simple discs that constitute the units of the "backbone" (that is, the vertebrae) in the lobe fins became transformed into interlocking structures that with the help of ligaments and muscles formed a strong horizontal column for the support of the body. At two points this vertebral column was supported by girdles; the pectoral girdle in front and the pelvic at the back. These two in turn were supported by the limbs and feet at-

A view of the gloomy green swamp forest which during Carboniferous times covered a large part of the earth. The scaly, long-snouted amphibian on the left has just caught a limbless

aquatic amphibian, and to the right a ponderous stegocephalian is on its way into the water. Farther back crawls a primitive reptile, the personification of the future. Across the middle soars a giant dragonfly.

tached to them. In order to move around, the limbs served not only to hold the body up against the force of gravity but also to propel the animal forward. Here we can see one of the many examples of change in function of homologous structures in the course of evolution. In the fish locomotion was effected mainly by sinuous movements of the body and tail with the spinal column acting as a stiffening rod—the paired fins served mainly a balancing function. In the first tetrapods the tail became thinned out to serve as a balancer of sorts, and the paired appendages took over most of the locomotor function with the vertebral column constituting the main horizontal girder. This pattern of locomotion, initiated but not "perfected" by the first amphibians, has continued with many variations through the evolution of the land-living vertebrates. The ancient **labyrinthodonts,** as the most common and numerous assemblage among the Carboniferous amphibians was called, were still relatively clumsy on land, and to this day if we watch a salamander we can see it twisting its body in a fishlike manner as it cumbrously moves forward, with its limbs extended practically at right angles to the trunk.

The amphibians made several great advances in their adaptation to life on land, but they never solved the problem of reproducing themselves away from the water. Present-day amphibians such as frogs and salamanders (and we must assume the same for their ancestors) generally deposit both sperm and ova into the water. The fertilized eggs develop into aquatic larvae (tadpoles) that go through a fishlike, gill-breathing stage before they metamorphose to become truly amphibious adults with limbs and lungs. It remained for the reptiles to attain complete independence of a watery environment, as we shall see later on.

Nevertheless, the amphibians, thanks to the uniform climate and wide-stretching swamps, were able to spread over the greater part of the world and develop along many different lines. The most common were the thick-skulled, alligator-like labyrinthodonts (also called **stegocephalians),** some of which returned to the water and became wholly aquatic types. Many genera grew to a considerable size, such as *Eryops,* six feet or more in length.

In addition to the semiterrestrial to

Diplocaulus.

78

wholly aquatic labyrinthodonts there were other groups of amphibians which were adapted to certain ecological niches not exploited by their big, multitudinous cousins. Some were small elongated snakelike forms without legs, such as *Dolichosoma*. Others, such as *Diplocaulus*, became tremendously flattened with broad sideways extensions of the skull.

The Carboniferous and early Permian periods could be called the **Age of Amphibians,** except that, about halfway towards the end, this "reign" was already being shared with the first reptiles, soon to become overwhelmingly numerous and diversified.

Although, as we shall see, the reptiles were from their very beginnings better suited to a wholly terrestrial existence than were the amphibians, they by no means suppressed their primitive but persistent forebears. For a long time reptiles and amphibians lived side by side, and some of the large Permian labyrinthodonts (such as *Eryops*) were probably able to compete fairly well with their reptilian contemporaries. Then, too, the uniformity of climate and a generally swampy environment would be very favorable to an adaptive radiation of amphibians.

However, with the close of the Carboniferous and the advent of the Permian, a change of environments took place. There were uplifts of the continental areas—the ancestral Alps in Europe and the first Rockies and the earliest Appalachians in North America were in the process of being gradually formed. With this change in the topography of the land there were related shifts in world climates. The uniformity so characteristic of the Carboniferous age gave way to varied conditions and surroundings. Instead of perpetually humid conditions there was probably an alternation of wet and dry seasons during the year. Local environments varied from swamps, streams, and ponds to dry uplands. In these diversified situations of the Permian period the reptiles began to replace the amphibians, although some of the latter (large aquatic forms) were able to hang on successfully well into the Mesozoic Era.

The particular "patent" that can be credited with the ultimate success of the reptiles was the development of a special type of egg—called the **amniote egg**— which provided its own little reservoir of fluid for the growing embryo.

THE REPTILES ASCEND THE THRONE

The appearance of the amniote egg, the germ cell with the built-in aquarium for the developing embryo, was a step of momentous magnitude—perhaps equal in importance to the first appearances of jaws and of limbs. Since the growing fetus cannot stand direct exposure to the air, the soft, gelatinous egg of amphibians has to be hatched in a fluid medium. Thus in their reproductive processes the tie to the water was still not broken, and the labyrinthodonts and other amphibians, although air-breathing, four-legged creatures, had really never quite achieved the full transition from water to land.

While the labyrinthodonts were still enjoying their undisputed possession of the swampy paradise afforded by the coal forests, an insignificant-appearing side branch was already beginning to go its own way. These were rather small ani-

mals. *Seymouria* of the Permian gives us a good picture of what these early forms looked like. To this day it is impossible to state with certainty whether *Seymouria* is an amphibian or a reptile. It is one of those intermediate forms which show characteristics of each of the groups it links. Since the fossil record cannot tell us anything about the type of egg it laid, we can really never be sure of its exact status. However, anatomically *Seymouria* is about as close to a "missing link" between amphibians and reptiles as could be wished for. It, itself, is not the ancestral form of all reptiles since it appears too late in the record. Contemporaneously with it there already existed many different kinds of true reptiles. As so often happens, *Seymouria* simply represents a fairly unmodified descendant from a lineage that at some earlier date gave rise

Seymouria, a form intermediate between amphibians and reptiles.

to an evolutionary sequence which became markedly distinct in the course of time.

While the female amphibians were waddling out into the water to lay their eggs, the stem reptiles must have been making their way instead to hollows in the ground on the banks of the swamp. Their eggs were not soft, gelatinous clumps but were enclosed in a hard, leathery shell and furnished with a large amount of yolk. But the most important fact about the reptile egg was the membrane called the **amnion** which permitted the embryo to go through the "tadpole" stage and remain within the egg away from water until it had become a fully developed land animal; the shell provided protection against desiccation, and the yolk supplied the embryo with the necessary nutrition.

The earliest reptiles were in many ways very similar anatomically and in external appearance to amphibians. However, there were clear-cut differences, and these primitive saurians formed the central stock from which all subsequent land vertebrates—not only reptiles, but also birds and mammals—developed. By the Permian period the radiation of reptiles into many different lineages was already well on the way.

As a group, the reptiles can be called "progressive" beyond the amphibian level, in terms of the following adaptations to a fully terrestrial existence: the amniote egg, a more efficient circulatory system, a better developed brain, more efficient walking and running limbs, and the possession of scales over their whole body to prevent loss of body fluids through evaporation from the skin.

Let us now turn to the Mesozoic Era which has justifiably been called the **Age of Reptiles.** It began with the close of the Paleozoic Era (at the end of the Permian) about 200 million years ago, and it lasted for approximately 130 million years. The Mesozoic Era is divided into three periods: the **Triassic,** the **Jurassic,** and the **Cretaceous,** lasting 35, 35, and 60 million years respectively.

As mentioned before, the Permian was a period of varied climates and environments which favoured the development of the reptiles so that they became the truly dominant land animals. Geological evidence indicates that this was true for the Triassic period to an even greater extent. Lands were mostly above sea level (somewhat more than presently perhaps). Evidently all the land bridges mentioned previously were emergent, with sufficiently amenable climates, even though locally varied, to permit reptiles (and also some still existent amphibians) to spread all over the world. Many of the continental deposits show no break at all between the close of the Permian and the beginning of the Triassic—however, the marine deposits show drastic differences, and the Permo-Triassic transition must have been a critical time for many of the seagoing animals, both vertebrate fishes as well as most of the invertebrates.

The advent of the Jurassic period is marked by marine incursions, so that many lands that had been extensive during late Triassic became restricted, with shallow seas advancing over many of the continental regions. In addition, some areas of the world appear to have been mostly desert—and therefore barren of tetrapod fossils. In the late Jurassic, environmental conditions as well as the fauna were very similar in North America, Europe, and Africa. Apparently then —in spite of much land submergence—

the intercontinental bridges must have been above water intermittently. Lands were low and covered with tropical jungles, with widespread swamps and uniformly warm temperatures. North America was probably cut in two by a shallow sea that spread from the Gulf of Mexico diagonally across the continent up to the Arctic. Europe consisted of many low islands and long peninsulas fingering out from mainland areas, so that it perhaps looked somewhat like the present-day East Indian archipelago.

During the last phase of the Mesozoic, the Cretaceous, the inland seas retreated from most of North America, but Europe was left much as during the Jurassic— a broken-up mass of large and small islands. The Cretaceous was a time of modernization in the plant world when the ferns, horsetails, and primitive **gymnosperms** such as the **cycads** (palmlike plants with feathery tops) and **gingkos,** characteristic of the first half of the Mesozoic, began to give way to the true **conifers** (pines, spruces, etc.) and later to the **angiosperms,** the deciduous trees (oaks, elms, etc.) and other flowering plants which give the world we know its familiar appearance.

The **stem reptiles** are all lumped together under the name of **cotylosaurs.** These gave rise during late Carboniferous and Permian times to all the major divisions of the class Reptilia.

Among the first and most important groups of reptiles we find the **turtles,** the **mammal-like reptiles,** and the **thecodonts** (or ancestral **archosaurians** —the "ruling reptiles").

The turtles have crawled and swum from the Triassic period through to our times almost unchanged for millions of years. They are believed to be an early and specialized cotylosaur offshoot. *Eunotosaurus,* a Permian form with curiously flattened ribs, found in South Africa, may be an ancestral **chelonian.** The protective shells of turtles are formed in part by a joining together of greatly expanded ribs. The flat, broad ribs of *Eunotosaurus* give an appearance indicating the beginnings of such a process. True turtles have been found very commonly from the Triassic on.

Our best records for the development of the mammal-like reptiles (or **synapsids**) are from the Permian of South Africa and North America. Over the course of time they acquired more and more mammal-like characteristics, particularly in the lower jaw and the teeth. Reptiles swallow their food mostly without any real chewing or grinding action, and their teeth are all alike—simple peg-like structures in most of them. However, among the synapsids we see a trend toward tooth differentiation into **incisors** (front teeth) for gripping and cutting, **canines** (eyeteeth) for tearing, and **premolars** and **molars** (cheek teeth) for masticating. The lower jaw, too, which in reptiles consists of many bones (just as in fishes and amphibians), tended to develop emphasis in the direction of only one large element. This is the **single** bone that forms each side of the mammalian lower jaw. Some of the bones

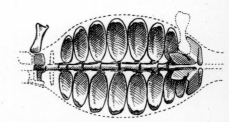

Skeleton of *Eunotosaurus*—a possible ancestor of the turtles.

that were no longer used in the new type of jaw articulation became incorporated into the middle ear. Instead of just the stapes, mammals have two other bones in their middle ear. In other words, structures which served to hold skull and lower jaw together in reptiles, when superseded by other elements in this function, became "utilized" in an entirely different fashion. They were added to the stapes (a part of the old hyoid arch of fishes), and together with it they went to form a chain of three ossicles that help in the conduction of sound from the air to the inner ear of mammals. This is really a fascinating story in change of function of homologous parts, and it is well documented with evidence from anatomy, embryology, and paleontology. It is among the synapsids that all these changes occurred, and we now have fossil evidence for all the above-outlined steps. There were even forms that had both the reptilian and mammalian type of jaw articulation side by side in the skull.

These mammal-like reptiles of South Africa (as well as Eurasia and South America) were a very varied assemblage. Some were predominantly herbivorous —the rather clumsy looking **dicynodonts,** such as *Endothiodon*—while another group included carnivores capable of rapid movement—the **theriodonts,** such as *Cynognathus,* about the size of a large dog. The earliest synapsids were already present by the very end of the Carboniferous. During the Permian they were fairly common in North America. They are called **pelycosaurs**—and the most primitive among them were probably fish-eating forms. They had a small radiation of their own into carnivorous and herbivorous lineages. *Dimetrodon* was a large (about eight feet long) flesh

Mammal-like reptiles from South Africa. Herbivorous dicynodonts in the background, and the carnivorous theriodont *Cynognathus* in front.

eater with a most curious structure on its back. The vertebral spines all along the backbone were tremendously elongated (several feet in height), and in life a "sail" of skin must have been spread from neck to tail. *Edaphosaurus* belonged to the herbivorous group of pelycosaurs, and it, too, bore a "sail". The purpose of these odd encumbrances is really not at all clear. An appealing suggestion that has been made is that the extra surface of skin stretched along the back would make an excellent heat regulator, since it would speedily absorb and lose radiant heat from the sun. Since reptiles are "cold"-blooded and depend entirely on their surroundings for their heat requirements (which are actually very close to the temperature at which the "warm"-

Ophiacodon, a very primitive American fish-eating pelycosaur.

blooded mammals operate), these sails might have enabled the pelycosaurs to get their heat ration relatively rapidly as soon as the sun came out in the morning. Then too, if they got overheated, the additional skin surface would permit a quick drop in body temperature as soon as they retreated to the shade.

It appears likely that the **therapsids** (including both the dicynodonts and theriodonts discussed previously) had a pelycosaurian ancestry. One particular theriodont branch gave rise to the **ictidosaurs** (some of which had *both* the reptilian and mammalian jaw articulation). Some of these in turn evolved into the *true* mammals.

Quite obviously many of the "advanced" synapsids must already have been warm-blooded and covered with hair, but of course this is something a fossil cannot tell us directly. We can only conclude this from other evidence, such as a whole assortment of typical mammal-like features in their skeletons. The first true mammals (and by definition this includes only forms with a single element on each side of the lower jaw) appear in the Triassic. They were tiny creatures, of which we possess only fragmentary remains. The hour of their destiny lay a hundred million years in the future, for the reptiles were the supreme rulers of the entire Mesozoic Era. It was only *after* the Cretaceous that the mammals were to become important.

The archosaurians (or "ruling reptiles") were all derived from a **thecodont** ancestry. Many of these were small, swift, **bipedal** forms. That is, they walked on

"Sail"-bearing pelycosaurs. In the foreground, the vegetarian *Edaphosaurus*, and immediately behind it, the carnivore *Dimetrodon*.

their hind limbs only, and their arms were free to be used as prehensile tools. *Saltoposuchus* is a good example of a small generalized Triassic thecodont. The **pseudosuchians** are the line whose early generalized representatives gave rise independently at various times to the **dinosaurs,** the **crocodiles,** the **pterosaurs** (or flying reptiles), and the **birds.** The other thecodont grouping comprises the **phytosaurs,** large quadrupedal carnivores—very similar to crocodiles in outward appearance.

Besides the archosaurians there appear in the Triassic forms that are thought to be the ancestors of the **lizards** and **snakes** (which are put together into a single grouping—the **Squamata**) and also possibly of the **rhynchocephalians.** A single living species, the tuatara (genus *Sphenodon*) of New Zealand is the last survivor of this order of reptiles. Lizards, snakes, and rhynchocephalians have been placed into one large category—the **lepidosaurians**—as opposed to the whole archosaurian assemblage. Snakes are probably derived from burrowing lizards that have forfeited their limbs in an adaptation to life underground.

Now to get back to the ruling reptiles. As a general designation the term "dinosaurs", which literally means "terrible lizards", can be misleading; many of them, despite the pompous name, were no bigger than lizards—and besides, they are not a natural grouping.

Dinosaurs really consist of two distinct orders: the **Saurischia** and the **Ornithischia** ("birdlike pelvis"), quite different in many features of their anatomy, particularly in the structure of the pelvic girdles. The Saurischia appeared in the Triassic and they gave rise to the largest terrestrial carnivores of all time

Sphenodon, a living rhynchocephalian.

as well as the most colossal plant eaters the world has ever known.

The latter are called **sauropods.** They were the real giants among dinosaurs and they culminated during the Jurassic in almost incredibly enormous specimens. Some, for example, the American genus *Apatosaurus* (commonly known as *Brontosaurus*) and *Brachiosaurus* from Africa and North America, were from sixty to eighty feet in length. They must have weighed over forty tons, and in order to bear the enormous load of their bodies, the sauropods had reverted to walking on all fours. Their necks were long and slender and could lift their startlingly small heads thirty feet or so into the air.

Although the sauropods are impressive because of their physical size, their intellectual capacity must have been alarmingly small. Their real brains were tiny compared to the large co-ordination centre located in the nerve cord in the region where their hind legs articulated with the body. Such a swelling of the nerve cord is characteristic of all tetrapods—but due to the sauropod's incongruously small head containing a typically unexpanded reptilian brain, this "second brain" (as it is often erroneously referred to) looks tremendous in proportion.

Incidentally, the sauropods spent the greater part of their lives eating. An indi-

Late Jurassic landscape: The gigantic sauropod dinosaur *Brontosaurus,* who must have weighed over thirty tons when alive.

vidual probably had to consume about a third of a ton of plant fodder daily, and with its weak teeth and relatively small mouth it must have taken all day to get through such a quantity. Their massive legs speak for the fact that the sauropods were capable of walking about on land, but probably they preferred to wade around on the bottom of shallow lakes where the buoyancy of the water would take some of the enormous weight off their limbs. As they only needed to have their nostrils above the surface of the water, they were able to remain at considerable depths and thus could keep well out of the way of the carnivorous dinosaurs, continuing to gorge themselves undisturbed on juicy aquatic

Brachiosaurus, a fifty-ton sauropod, had nostrils located high up on the forehead.

plants of the lake. *Brachiosaurus* had adapted itself to this amphibian way of life by having its nostrils placed high on top of its forehead. Today we find the giant skeletons of sauropods in former lakes and swamps where their remains had collected to become fossilized.

The sauropods persisted to the end of the Mesozoic Era. There were Cretaceous representatives in southern Argentina, India, and southern France, as well as in North America, but the majority of them were extinct before the Jurassic drew to a close.

Unlike most of the sauropods, the carnivorous saurischians—the **theropods**—all retained the upright gait of their thecodont forebears. The earliest theropods were small marauders (two to six feet in length), light and agile types with hollow bones. The strong birdlike hind limbs supported the body at the hips, and there was a long tail to counterbalance the body in front of the pelvis. The forelimbs were relatively short, and the hands were adapted for grasping. During the Triassic these light running types (the **coelurosaurs,** as they are called) were fairly common but became rare during the Jurassic. One American form, *Ornitholestes,* however, is found fairly frequently in the upper Jurassic. It had only three grasping digits to each hand, and some people imagined it might have lived on the con-

temporaneous primitive birds. This is probably a fallacy; presumably small reptiles such as lizards and the small early mammals were the staple articles of diet of this and the other small dinosaurs.

In addition to the coelurosaur lineage there was another line of development among the theropods. This other group was characterized by a trend towards an over-all extreme massiveness—the skull particularly undergoing a tremendous relative size increase together with a progressive reduction of the front limbs, so the arms and hands became almost vestigial in some of the giant Cretaceous forms.

Teratosaurus, one of the few large carnivorous dinosaurs of the Triassic period. Two small bipedal coelurosaurs in the foreground.

This trend had already begun to manifest itself in the Triassic—and we find forms like *Teratosaurus* in Europe, *Anchisaurus* in North America, and others in South Africa, that were distinguished from their contemporaries by the possession of a large skull with compressed recurved teeth. It is from such forms that the large flesh-eating dinosaurs of the Jurassic stem.

Ornitholestes,—a Jurassic carnivorous dinosaur.

Allosaurus was a thirty-five-feet-long Jurassic theropod, quite capable of attacking even the mightiest of the contemporaneous sauropods and other herbivorous dinosaurs. Its arms and clawed hands, though relatively small, were still capable of being used as an aid to feeding. Its skull was over two feet long with tight rows of murderous daggerlike teeth.

The other order of dinosaurs—the Ornithischia—first appeared in the Jurassic, and from the beginning they were a strictly herbivorous assemblage. The most primitive forms were still predominantly bipedal, with some of them remaining that way—but the majority of the Ornithischia returned to a quadrupedal mode of existence.

Camptosaurus of the Jurassic of North America and Europe and *Iguanodon* of the early Cretaceous of Europe are among the best known of the primitive bipedal ornithischians—the **ornithopods.** *Camptosaurus* was a small- to medium-sized dinosaur (some species were about six feet in length, others as long as twenty feet). It had strong hind limbs, but the front legs were sufficiently robust so that a four-legged mode of progression was certainly possible, if this dinosaur so desired (when browsing on vegetation, for instance). The skull was already specialized in the ornithischian direction, with special adaptations in the jaw mechanism for efficiently grinding up food. *Iguanodon* was essentially an enlarged camptosaur, about thirty feet long and in possession of a peculiarly spiked thumb that must have served as a weapon of defence.

The Ornithischia in general tended to produce some really bizarre forms. Among their oddest representatives can be numbered the primarily Jurassic **stegosaurs** (or **plated dinosaurs**)—essentially enlarged camptosaurs that had reverted secondarily to a four-footed mode of locomotion and developed peculiar plates on the back and spikes on the tail. The best-known genus is *Stegosaurus,* characterized by a double row of alternately spaced, triangular-shaped, bony plates down the middle of its back and tail. These "wedges" were vertical in position since their thickened bases were embedded in the flesh of the back. *Stegosaurus,* although over twenty feet in length, had a relatively tiny skull, and it, too, is re-

Stegosaurus, a plated dinosaur. The dotted line represents the central nervous system. Notice the tiny brain compared to the large co-ordination centre for the control of the hind limbs.

Protosuchus, the first known crocodilian

nowned for its "second brain" being larger than the real structure which was about the size of an egg. It had four long bony spikes on its muscular tail, which must have constituted a powerful mace-like weapon of defence.

As previously mentioned, the archosaurians also include the crocodilians. The oldest known crocodile ancestor is *Protosuchus,* some three to four feet in length, found in deposits at the Triassic and Jurassic transition zone in Arizona. The back and belly were protected by solid bony plates (called **scutes**), and even the tail was enclosed in a solid, segmented chain mail. It is doubtful that

Protosuchus was a contemporary of the large phytosaurs so characteristic of Triassic times, for these crocodile-like thecodonts had become extinct at the end of the Triassic. With the beginning of the Jurassic, the crocodilians quickly filled the ecological niche left vacant by the phytosaurs which had been remarkably similar in outward appearance as well as habits. One obvious and distinctive difference, however, between crocodiles and phytosaurs is in the position of the nasal openings. The phytosaurs had theirs on the forehead just in front of the elongation of the skull that forms the snout. Crocodilians have their external nares located at the tip of the muzzle. The replacement of the phytosaurs by the crocodilians is one of those unexplained and frequent occurrences in the fossil record, where a group becomes extinct and their vacated niche is filled by another not directly related group that was never in direct competition or even contemporaneous with its predecessors.

The first crocodilians to evolve from

A phytosaur

Animal life in North America during the upper Jurassic period, about 150 million years ago. The pterodactyls in the top left-hand corner are gliding over *Camptosaurus*. In front is plated and spiked *Stegosaurus,* as big as a modern elephant and with a brain the size of a walnut. In the background,

a protosuchian ancestry were the **meso-suchians** (such as *Teleosaurus*), existing abundantly from the lower Jurassic to the end of the Cretaceous and straggling into the Tertiary period. Many of these were fish-eating types living along the shores of the Jurassic seas. There was even one family (the **geosaurs**) that became completely ocean going—developing flippers and a tail fin.

The more familiar line of advanced crocodilians are the **eusuchians,** the crocodiles, alligators, and gavials of the modern world. These appeared during the Cretaceous, and they evolved rapidly to displace their direct ancestors, the mesosuchians.

The crocodilians are a tough race. They have not only survived the extinction of the closely related dinosaurs, but they have also watched the mammals go through their whole range of evolution, from the first shrewlike little creature to the modern, rifle-bearing,

Allosaurus, the largest carnivorous dinosaur of Jurassic times, is in the process of finishing up its prey. On the bottom right, *Archaeopteryx,* a very primitive and still reptile-like bird, is being attacked by nimble-footed *Ornitholestes.*

white safari hunter. If it were not for the latter and other greedy members of the species *Homo sapiens* anxious to get at their leathery hides, the crocodilians would be in no danger of losing their position as a very successful reptile group adapted particularly to life in subtropical to tropical regions of the world.

Teleosaurus, a Jurassic mesosuchian, belonging to the group from which modern crocodilians are descended.

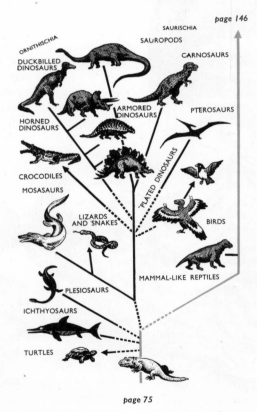

page 146

page 75

Phylogenetic Tree No. 6: Reptiles

"SEA MONSTERS" AND "FLYING DRAGONS"

The endless wide expanses of the ocean have a strange power over the mind of man and call forth a peculiar feeling of harmony in our consciousness. Whether such a poetic feeling about the original home of life has anything to do with the fact that every one of the mainland's large vertebrate groups has at some time in the earth's history sent ambassadors back to the sea from which life came is doubtful—still this is what did occur, and the Triassic marks the first time that land-living tetrapods turned in any appreciable numbers to a marine existence.

During their long evolutionary history the tetrapods had freed themselves from aquatic habits to become—as reptiles—animals that were finally completely independent of water. Now some of them went back to exploit the opportunities represented by oceans swarming with food in the form of numerous fishes (mainly holosteans), molluscs, and other invertebrates. Such a return to the ancestral "domicile" involved the assumption of the old problems with which their fish ancestors had contended in the dim past —how to stay afloat and move through the water, and how to propagate themselves away from the land. All these problems were solved by the highly successful marine reptile lineages in one way or another, the solutions always entailing modifications of the various adaptations that had made reptiles efficient and independent land-living animals. Gravity and desiccation were no longer challenges, but buoyancy and propulsion through the water were. Legs and feet became finlike paddles; tails developed to resemble the caudal fins of fishes. Reptile eggs that cannot develop in sea water either have to be laid on land, to the risk of the female (marine turtles are an example), or "hatched" inside the body—the young being born live. This was the solution hit upon by certain of the completely marine types, and this is the method employed today by many of the sea snakes of the Indian Ocean. (This type of reproduction is not like the live birth of mammals but involves the development of a regular yolky reptile egg inside the female.)

But, whatever the modification, the tetrapod heritage can be clearly demonstrated—the lungs were retained, and a close study of the skeleton reveals all these marine vertebrates as the true reptiles that they were. So in one sense there was a reversal of evolution—from aquatic fishes to intermediate amphibian and reptile ancestors to aquatic reptilian descendants. But the history of these last really did not go the *full* cycle; they never became fishes—those they could never be again. Evolution always builds on what has gone before, and the step-by-step architecture can always be deciphered by the discerning eye.

Already during late Carboniferous

times there appeared, together with the first recorded cotylosaurs or stem reptiles, a relatively unimportant and specialized offshoot, the **mesosaurs**—they had broad paddles for limbs and a deep tail clearly designed for swimming. Their elongated tooth-rimmed jaws were ideal fish traps. However, they were not marine types, since from the nature of the sediments in which these reptiles are found preserved it appears likely that they lived in fresh-water streams and ponds.

Unmistakably marine groups appear in the Triassic. Among the first were the **placodonts** (e.g., *Placodus*). These were specialized for life in shallow marine waters where they fed on shelled molluscs that they picked off the sea bottom and then crushed between their flat, platelike teeth. They were stout-bodied, short-necked forms with rather small paddles for limbs. Some genera had a turtlelike carapace on their backs, made up of coalesced scutes. Contemporaneous with the placodonts were the **nothosaurs** (e.g., *Nothosaurus*), which reached the height of their development in late Triassic times. These were small- to medium-sized elongated reptiles with very long, sinuous necks. The limbs were rather long, and the feet were modified as paddles. However, like modern seals and sea lions, they were probably able to come out on land. They fed on fish which they caught by darting their neck back and forth.

This mode of living and feeding was "perfected" by the **plesiosaurs** which essentially followed the nothosaur pattern and which succeeded these Triassic forms to become world-wide in distribution and extremely numerous during Jurassic and Cretaceous times. (Most authorities place the placodonts, notho-

saurs, and plesiosaurs together into one grouping—the **sauropterygians**—since they think that these marine reptiles are closely enough related to deserve a common ancestor. It is felt that such an ancestral sauropterygian is to be sought among certain Permian land forms, early derivatives of the cotylosaurs.) Many of the Jurassic plesiosaurs were giants of over forty feet. One line among them followed

Triassic *Nothosaurus,* a member of the group which may have given rise to the plesiosaurs.

Above: *Mesosaurus*, an aquatic reptile probably inhabiting bodies of fresh water during the late Carboniferous or early Permian period. Centre: An early ichthyosaur from the Triassic. Below: A mollusc-eating placodont, *Placodus*, from the same period.

the nothosaur habit of rowing through shoals of fish to catch their prey by darting their tremendously elongated necks back and forth. Another line followed a trend towards increase in skull size, mainly through a prodigious lengthening of the jaws (some forms had heads twelve feet long), and their necks were comparatively short. These had a more streamlined shape than the others. The plesiosaurs as a group were characterized by big paddle-shaped flippers which they used more or less like oars, and they were anything but graceful in appearance. Some of the long-necked forms have been aptly described as resembling nothing so much as a snake pulled through the body of a turtle.

The ichthyosaurs were completely adapted to life in the high seas.

Plesiosaurs in the Jurassic seas of Europe.

In broad contrast to the rather cumbersome sauropterygian assemblage stand the wonderfully streamlined **ichthyosaurs**. These made their home in the open sea and were the most completely marine-adapted of all oceangoing reptiles. They first appear fully fledged during the Triassic, and we can only surmise that their ancestors were Permian land reptiles related to the cotylosaurs. The ichthyosaurs swam like fishes, using the driving force of the tail to propel themselves forward, with their finlike flippers serving as balancing structures. *Ichthyosaurus* is a typical Jurassic representative even more fishlike than the somewhat less specialized Triassic forms. From impressions of the whole body in black shale deposits we know that the ichthyosaurs even had a fleshy fin on the back to take the place of the bony dorsal fin of fishes. The end of the spinal column was turned down with a fleshy lobe above simulating a typical fish tail. In their habits as well as appearance they can be compared to the big mackerels and tunas of our oceans and also with their mammalian counterparts, the porpoises, which were to take to the water long after the ichthyosaurs had become extinct at the end of the Cretaceous. *Ichthyosaurus* had a wreath of bony plates around its large eyes to protect these all important sense organs against the pressure of the water. Thanks to the sharp teeth in its dolphinlike snout, it was able to snap up prey without reducing speed as it tore through the waves. There exist fossils of *Ichthyosaurus* that show its embryos in position inside the body cavity of the adult. In one specimen the skull of an embryo is located in the pelvic region as if the little ichthyosaur was in the process of being born when death overtook the female. These forms then were able to give birth to live young—an absolute necessity for such completely aquatic creatures whose eggs, being reptilian, could not develop in sea water. The sauropterygians were probably not capable of such a method of reproduction but dragged themselves up on shore to deposit eggs in nests dug in the sand.

The ichthyosaurs and the sauropterygians dominated the Triassic and Jurassic seas. During the latter period they were joined by the geosaurs, the wholly marine crocodilians mentioned before, and in the Cretaceous another reptilian lineage —this time the Squamata—sent a branch into the ocean to join the plesiosaurs and ichthyosaurs, still numerous at that time. These squamates were true lizards—the **mosasaurs,** which will be described in the next chapter.

The saurians did not restrict their supremacy to the sea and the land. The Mesozoic Era was still young when some reptiles took to the air at the beginning of the Jurassic period and, as the first vertebrates to do so, overcame the force of gravity. These flying reptiles are called **pterosaurs.** They were archosaurians that became adapted to flight. In so doing they had to modify their structure in order to satisfy the extremely rigorous requirements that exist for any flying vertebrate. The biggest problem, of course, is the downward pull of gravity. Thus comparative lightness in relation to the muscles that move the wings is of the essence. Therefore, thin but strong bones that are hollow internally characterize the pterosaurs (as well as the birds). Wings developed by transformations in the forelimbs. A flight surface was provided by a thin membrane stretched between the enormously elongated fourth finger on each side and the relatively small and weak hind limbs. The fingers in front of the fourth digit were reduced to small hooks that may have been used as hangers for roosting in trees or on cliffs; the fifth finger was lost. The bottom part of the pectoral girdle (the breastbone) became enlarged to serve as an area of origin for large pectoral muscles that moved the wings. Since flight necessitates a delicate sense of balance, that part of the brain especially concerned with this function, namely the **cerebellum** (located towards the rear), is particularly large and well developed in flying vertebrates. That this was also the case with pterosaurs can be demonstrated from internal casts made of the brain cavity in the preserved skull.

The early forms, such as the two-feet-long *Rhamphorhynchus,* had a very long tail, and impressions in the rock indicate that it ended in a rudder-shaped membrane at the tip. The front of the skull and jaws were elongated and supplied with long, pointed, forwardly projecting teeth forming an ideal trap for the fish that were probably its staple diet. It must have fed by swooping down and catching fish swimming at the surface of lakes or lagoons.

During the Jurassic there were various

Pterosaurs of Jurassic age. Both are tailed forms. *Rhamphorhynchus* in the right-hand corner had a rudder-like structure at the end of its long tail.

pterosaurs similar to the long-tailed *Rhamphorhynchus*—the **rhamphorhyn- choids.** However, in late Jurassic times another group of pterosaurs, the **ptero- dactyloids,** appeared as an offshoot from the long-tailed forms. These pterosaurs had a much reduced tail—it was just a little nubbin in some. The jaws became very much like a bird beak in the ad- vanced members of this group, teeth no longer being present. The pterodactyl- oids developed some gigantic forms (which will be described in the next chapter) but became extinct towards the end of the Cretaceous. Many people have wondered whether the pterosaurs may not have had some insulating covering such as hair and been an independently warm-blooded group (like birds and mammals), since it is hard to imagine that the high energy requirements set by a flying mode of existence could have been met satisfactorily by the typically low rate of metabolism common to rep- tiles. Since fossil evidence for these

points does not exist, they must remain in the realm of conjecture. However, we can be pretty sure why the pterosaurs became extinct. By late Cretaceous times the birds, a separate offshoot from the archosaur stock, were becoming modern- ized, and they—being obviously much more efficient flying vertebrates than the pterosaurs could ever have been—prob- ably displaced the latter.

The vertebrates that really came to dom- inate the air are the birds. They, like the pterosaurs, appeared in Jurassic times, and they, like the flying reptiles, were descended from an archosaurian ances- try. The first birds are known to us from two specimens (about the size of a crow), called *Archaeopteryx,* that were preserved down to the finest detail of their skin covering in a lithographic limestone formed in a shallow tropical lagoon into which these flying vertebrates must have —very fortunately for us—fallen.

Were it not for the impression of

feathers, *Archaeopteryx,* with its typical thecodont skull, toothed jaws, dinosaur-like pelvis, long tail, and still separate clawed digits, would have been classified without much question as a typical reptile. It is only the clear imprints of perfectly formed wing, body, and tail feathers that make *Archaeopteryx* the first bird. Anatomically, even today's birds, which have gone a long way since this Jurassic forebear (by developing a much lightened skull with a horny, toothless beak, fused hand bones that support the long wing feathers, a very strongly keeled breastbone for powerful pectoral muscles, and a short stumpy tail remnant for the support of the fanned-out tail feathers, in addition to many other adaptations to an aerial way of life), can be and have been considered nothing but "glorified flying archosaurians". Physiologically they show many advances over the typical reptilian level of organization in that birds are warm-blooded and have a more efficient circulatory system (similar but not homologous to that of mammals). In their nervous system, however, birds are essentially reptiles with an enlarged cerebellum (for increased balance sensitivity—as in the pterosaurs). Their mode of reproduction is very similar to that of reptiles—laying as they do a characteristically shelled, heavily yolked amniote egg.

The possession of insulating feathers by *Archaeopteryx* leads us to the well-founded conclusion that already in the Jurassic birds had an efficient temperature-control system. The flight surface provided by the thin and easily torn structure that was the pterosaur wing membrane cannot be compared in durability and aerial efficiency to the feathered bird's wings. Whereas pterosaurs were probably mainly soaring, passively gliding forms which coasted with the air

Archaeopteryx.

currents, and which might have been capable to some extent of operating at constant temperatures, birds were definitely warm-blooded, actively flying, aerial vertebrates from the Cretaceous on. (The Jurassic *Archaeopteryx* looks like a poor flyer.) They probably started to replace the pterosaurs at that time.

Two theories have been advanced to account for the evolution of flight in birds. One postulates a bipedal running thecodont ancestor which flapped its forelimbs and developed feathers (these can be demonstrated to be nothing but modified scales) on them to help it along in its running on the ground. Gradually, through mutation and selection, the wings enlarged to become organs of flight rather than accessories to rapid locomotion on the ground. Adherents of the other theory see bird ancestors as climbing reptiles which developed feathered forelimbs for gliding down to the ground or onto other trees, in the manner of modern "flying" squirrels. Eventually these supports for gliding became large enough to enable their bearers to fly.

When theorizing about the evolution of wings in the lineage that gave rise to the pterosaurs, the climbing and "parachuting" hypothesis seems the more applicable—as a matter of fact, it is doubtful that this aerial archosaur group ever achieved fully active flight to the same extent as birds have.

With the close of the Jurassic the reptile dynasty had only one more geological period left in which to dominate—the Cretaceous—during which there existed a truly spectacular diversity and abundance of forms among them before the extinction, unexplained to this day, of many of their proudest lineages.

THE CLIMAX AND DECLINE OF THE DINOSAURS

The archosaurians and other reptiles reached the peak of their development during the Cretaceous period. The whole earth was populated by—to us—strange and odd looking creatures, some of which were of truly gigantic proportions.

And then the inexplicable came to pass. Just when the star of the reptiles was apparently at its zenith, their most highly diversified representatives—the dinosaurs and the marine reptiles—vanished from the surface of the globe within such an incredibly short space of time that one can rightly speak—from a relative viewpoint—of sudden and abrupt extinction.

No riddle would appear to be more contradictory and difficult to fathom.

Why did many of the dinosaurs steadily become bigger and bigger, specialize in numerous distinct species adapted to every conceivable habitat, and then at the height of their radiation suddenly disappear from the fossil record? The answer is anything but clear-cut, and the cause appears to be anything but a single determining factor. However, before going into some of the possible reasons for this still not fully understood occurrence, let us try to reconstruct a living inventory of the truly remarkable creatures which dominated the Cretaceous period.

The trend toward massivity demonstrated by the Jurassic carnivorous dinosaur, the theropod *Allosaurus,* culminated in Cretaceous times with forms like *Gorgosaurus* and *Tyrannosaurus.* The last was forty feet long, stood about twenty feet high to the top of its head, and must have weighed from six to eight tons when alive. Its forelimbs were reduced to such an extent that they almost look ridiculous—two little "remnants" nearly lost from sight in the shadow of the tremendous head above. However, the two rows of six-inch-long sharply recurved teeth lining the awesome jaws furnish reassurance as to the carnivorous potential of this theropod—all its aggressivity was neatly packaged into one unit, namely the head, the arms not being needed at all when killing and feeding.

Another line of theropod evolution taking place among the lightly built types (the coelurosaurians discussed previously) during the Cretaceous period was marked by a moderate size increase and extreme specialization of the skull. This adaptational trend is typified by the late Cretaceous genus, *Ornithomimus*—a rapid-running bipedal form much like an ostrich. Its forelimbs were even longer and more grasping than those of the Jurassic *Ornitholestes.* Its most remarkable specialization, though, was the presence of a toothless, ostrichlike beak fitted to a small skull at the end of its long, sinuous neck.

The appearance and inferred mode of

life of *Ornithomimus* are paralleled to a striking extent by modern large flightless birds. Like these, it probably ate many different things—small reptiles, insects, fruits, and any other food it could get. It used to be thought that *Ornithomimus* was an eggeater, but probably eggs were simply just another item on the menu whenever they happened to be available.

The crocodilians were also going through a period of diversification during the Cretaceous. The eusuchians were beginning to replace the mesosuchians, and some like *Phobosuchus* reached a length of fifty feet. It is quite likely that this crocodile preyed upon the contemporaneous dinosaurs.

The Squamata (not archosaurs but belonging to the lepidosaurian assemblage mentioned earlier) were first represented by Jurassic lizards. These became a fairly flourishing group during the Cretaceous and are now very successful reptiles. During the Cretaceous one lizard family, the **varanids,** sent some of their members into the oceans as we shall see in a little while. Snakes are a specialized lizard offshoot and first appear in Cretaceous times; modern boas and pythons are little-modified descendants. Poisonous snakes did not develop until much later—during the Cenozoic Era.

The Ornithischia, as we have seen, were the other order of dinosaurs, and they in particular seemed to have specialized in bizarre forms. The Cretaceous period saw the origin, diversification, and extinction of several ornithischian groupings.

There were the **ankylosaurs,** or **armoured dinosaurs,** secondarily four-legged herbivores that had specialized in a type of defence mechanism that we find again much later in certain mammals (e.g., the glyptodonts and armadillos). *Ankylosaurus* was a characteristic genus. It was the living tank of the Cretaceous period and, thanks to its heavy armour of bony scutes, must have been an almost impenetrable fortress. There were sharp spikes along its sides, and its amoured tail ended in a massive lump of bone which could serve as a dangerous club if an enemy approached too closely.

The **ceratopsians,** or **horned dinosaurs,** were the last of the dinosaurs to evolve. They appeared in late Cretaceous times, and although their history was a brief one, they went through a remarkably varied range of adaptive radiation in the relatively brief span of time available to them—that is, until the end of the Cretaceous when they, along with so many others, became extinct. The ceratopsians, in opposition to the passive defence mechanisms adopted by the Jurassic stegosaurs and the Cretaceous ankylosaurs, went in for active counterattack in a fashion similar to the horned cattle of later times.

One of the last and most impressive representatives of this group was *Triceratops*. Some members of this genus were twenty feet long, with a skull almost six feet long if we include the **frill.** This last was a characteristic feature possessed by all ceratopsians, and it consisted of an extension of certain of the skull bones to form a slightly upward slanting "collar" over the neck nearly to the shoulders. The functional purpose of the frill was probably twofold. Besides serving as an area of attachment for strong jaw as well as powerful neck muscles, it probably also functioned as a protective device to cover the vital neck area. *Triceratops* had, in addition to

Tyrannosaurus—the biggest carnivore that ever walked the earth. Each of its daggerlike teeth was about five inches long. In the foreground is lumbering herbivorous *Ankylosaurus*, relying on its heavy armour for passive defence. Notice the flowering plants which became important during the Cretaceous period.

Ferocious *Gorgosaurus* facing impressively horned *Triceratops*.

its nasal horn, two others—one above each eye over the brows. These big ceratopsians, with their sharply pointed head weapons driven by powerful neck muscles as well as by the momentum of the heavy body, must have been a match for even the largest of the contemporaneous flesh-eating dinosaurs. The horned dinosaurs were probably something like rhinoceroses among living mammals. They were upland-dwelling herbivores, capable of actively warding off attack.

Protoceratops, representing the first true horned dinosaurs. These were small animals compared to the later giant representatives of the group.

The large ceratopsians seemed to have been restricted to North America. However, the first true horned dinosaurs, small quadrupedal forms already characterized by a bony frill extending out from the skull, but without large horns (a small nasal horn appearing only in the adult stages of the animals), are found in Mongolia as well as in North America. *Protoceratops* is the Asiatic genus, and during the nineteen twenties an American expedition discovered a large series of skeletons of this early ceratopsian showing all stages of growth from the newly born hatchling to the adult and even parts of embryos preserved in fossil eggs of which several nestfuls were dug up. *Leptoceratops,* the American genus, is very much like *Protoceratops,* and it, or forms very much like it, must have given rise to the other American horned dinosaurs. These were mostly large forms with a great variety of horn structures developing on the skull; the frill, too, showed much variability in its exact shape and configuration.

Psittacosaurus, also a Mongolian genus (from Cretaceous deposits), makes a good ancestral type for all the true ceratopsians. It is a rather generalized, still bipedal ornithischian, showing certain modifications in the skull (such as a hooklike beak overhanging the lower jaw) that appear to set the trend for later developments among the horned dinosaurs.

The **"duck-billed" dinosaurs,** or **hadrosaurs,** were a Cretaceous line of ornithopod development from primitive bipedal Jurassic ornithischians (such as *Camptosaurus,* described previously). They were the most spectacular and successful of the ornithopods, adapted to a semi-aquatic life on the swampy shores of late Cretaceous lakes and lagoons. They probably filled the ecological niche of the large sauropods, which by this time had become rare in many parts of the world.

The hadrosaurs (also called **trachodonts**) were bipedal dinosaurs attaining lengths of from thirty to forty feet. They had webbed toes and a powerful tail, probably used for sculling rapidly through the water when escaping from some predator. In front, their skull and lower jaws became broad and flat to form a sort of duck bill, hence their name. On each side of the jaw the hadrosaurs developed a solid pavement of approximately a thousand close-set, lozenge-shaped teeth—giving them a mouthful of approximately two thousand. A more efficient grinding mill for crushing plant food (as well as molluscs probably) could hardly be imagined.

Towards the end of the Cretaceous the duck-billed dinosaurs developed a number of different genera, especially conspicuous by unusual adaptations in the nasal region of the skull. In these forms the bones making up the front of the upper jaws and the nasal bones were pulled back over the top of the skull to produce a hollow crest. These crests took on many different shapes and forms in the various hadrosaurs so helmeted.

The "swollen" snout of *Kritosaurus* gave it a hawklike appearance; *Lambeosaurus* was distinguished by an axe-shaped crest; *Corythosaurus* had a domelike structure capping the skull; while *Parasaurolophus* had a long, hollow, tubular excrescence extending far back behind the head. The function of these crests has been a subject of debate. The most reasonable theory is that an extra air supply could be stored in these hollow chambers, enabling the trachodonts to stay submerged for long periods.

During the course of the Cretaceous period the pterodactyloids (or short-tailed pterosaurs) replaced the rhamphorhynchoids completely. Some of them developed a tremendous wingspread. *Pteranodon,* for instance, spanned twenty-five feet from wing tip to wing tip and in that sense was probably the largest flying creature that ever existed. However, its actual body was no larger than that of a turkey, illustrating the limitations set on size if a vertebrate becomes adapted for flight. *Pteranodon* (as well as other pterodactyloids) had special adaptations in the backbone for strengthening the attachment of the shoulder girdle, and it sported a long, backward-extended crest growing out of the skull. This structure may have served for the attachment of strong jaw muscles to close the long toothless beak, or it might have been a rudder and steering mechanism. Soaring gracefully over the Cretaceous seas, ready to pounce on surface-swimming fishes, these flying reptiles must have presented a wonderful spectacle.

Cretaceous birds were still primitive in that they retained some teeth in the jaws. Otherwise, however, they were typical birds. The bones of the hand were fused together as in modern birds; the pelvic girdle was firmly joined to the vertebral column; the long tail was suppressed; the bones were all highly pneumatic; and as the most marked change over the Jurassic genus *Archaeopteryx*, we find a tremendous enlargement of the breastbone—certain proof that flight had been fully perfected. Already in Cretaceous times a great adaptive radiation of birds must have taken place. For although we find only a few forms (this scarcity of fossil material also holds

"Duck-billed" dinosaurs with bizarre head combs. Above: *Corythosaurus* and *Kritosaurus*. Below: *Parasaurolophus* and *Lambeosaurus*

for all the future geologic periods, as would only be expected from the poor chances of preservation afforded to an aerial, hollow-boned assemblage like birds), these show a great diversity. In addition to obviously well-adapted flying

Two "duck-bills" *(Trachodon)* grubbing in the swamp. On the shore stands ostrichlike *Ornithomimus*.

ternlike creatures there was the genus *Hesperornis,* a bird specialized for swimming and diving in the fashion of modern loons. Several feet long, its body was rather streamlined, with powerful hind legs to give a strong paddling stroke. The wings had become suppressed —only vestigial arm bones remaining.

The Cretaceous seas were swarming with marine reptiles—some of them of gigantic size.

The plesiosaurs, following trends set during Jurassic times, developed some truly enormous forms. This size increase was noticeable among the short-necked group as well as in the long-necked types. For example, there was *Kronosaurus* among the former, with a skull twelve feet long. *Elasmosaurus* represents the culmination in upper Cretaceous times of the long-necked lineage; its neck was twice as long as its body and contained about eighty vertebrae.

The ichthyosaurs appear to have become relatively rare in Cretaceous times, and it looks as though this particular group of marine reptiles became extinct before the close of the period.

A new addition to the marine fauna of the Cretaceous were the mosasaurs, who (as mentioned before) were a specialized branch of varanid lizards. Some of them followed a trend towards giantism, as have so many ocean-living vertebrates, to culminate in forms like *Tylosaurus,* over thirty feet long. The mosasaurs were adapted to a marine life through a number of specializations. Their nostrils were located high on the skull; they had paddles for limbs, and their tail was deepened to form a powerful scull with which to drive themselves through the water. They were a very successful group while they lasted, becoming world-wide in their distribution. They became extinct near the end of the Cretaceous, but their close relatives, the varanid lizards that had stayed on land, have continued to the present day.

The Cretaceous oceans also harboured large representatives from among the turtles. There were giant marine turtles (for example, *Archelon,* which was twelve feet long), with their feet developed as broad, webbed flippers and their protective shell lightened by a reduction of the bony elements composing it. Modern marine turtles are little changed in appearance from these Cretaceous forms.

There was even a giant Cretaceous fish, namely the primitive teleost genus *Portheus,* members of which attained lengths of twelve feet. Modern herrings, salmon, and trout belong to the same group as did *Portheus.*

The invertebrates, too, developed some giant marine forms, particularly the cephalopods. The ammonoids, who by now had almost completely replaced their ancestors, the nautiloids, evolved coiled Cretaceous genera, some of which attained the size of tractor wheels—six and a half feet in diameter. However, both these as well as all the other ammonoids (many of which were much smaller) became extinct for unexplained reasons, as did the marine reptiles, at the end of the Cretaceous. The nautiloids straggled on, and one genus is with us today. Another group of common Cretaceous cephalopods were the **belemnoids,** which had appeared by late Paleozoic times. They had an internal shell and they probably looked very much like modern squids **(teuthoids)** and cuttlefishes **(sepioids),** both of which first show up in Jurassic deposits, and whose ancestors they are believed to have been. The belemnoids became sharply reduced in numbers at the end of the Cretaceous, but some genera survived into early Cenozoic times. The **octopoids,** or octopi, are also thought to be related to the belemnoids. The earliest octopus is known from an impression found in upper Cretaceous rocks. Octopi do not have any hard parts at all, not even the internal shell of belemnoids, squids, and cuttlefishes.

As the Cretaceous period drew to its close, all the reptiles with the exception of the crocodiles, the turtles, the lizards and snakes (the Squamata), and the fourth surviving (but very restricted) order—the rhynchocephalians—passed into extinction. This mysterious mass death is one of the unsolved riddles in the history of evolution. How could such a variety of animals, many of them giants and at the zenith of their adaptive radiation, disappear so relatively rapidly from the land, the sea, and the air, with only a "chosen few" left to continue the reptilian way of life?

No *one* obvious reason exists. A single explanation will never be sufficient. The extinction of most of the Mesozoic reptiles must be attributed to a fateful combination of a number of interrelated factors.

An encounter between reptilian giants of air and sea, the pterosaur *Pteranodon* and the mosasaur *Tylosaurus*.

The Cretaceous sea. In the lower part of the picture a giant marine turtle *(Archelon)* swims away. On the bottom, to the right lie some ammonoid shells, and above them swims a giant herring *(Portheus)*. Near the surface swim two loon-like toothed birds *(Hesperornis)*, and a plesiosaur is rearing its long neck next to them.

Geological upheavals undoubtedly played an important part. During the course of the Cretaceous period continental uplifts were in progress all over the world, and in their wake followed the drying up of lakes and marshes with, no doubt, some catastrophic consequences for the dinosaurs, adapted as many of them were to moist, swampy environments. The most marked of these disturbances was the **Laramide Revolu-** tion, a time of mountain building during which the Rockies and other ranges were elevated. This condition of rising lands probably brought about climatic shifts which are seen reflected in marked changes in the vegetation of the late Cretaceous. For it was then that the angiosperms, the present-day flowering plants (including the deciduous trees) probably evolving in restricted upland areas until now, began an "explosive" world-wide radiation. Helped by bees and other pollinating insects, the angiosperms, before the end of the Mesozoic Era, pushed the old vegetation of conifers and horsetails into a relatively minor role. Now it is conceivable that the herbivorous dinosaurs could not adapt their eating habits to these new plants—this would be disastrous for them as well as for the carnivorous dinosaurs to whom their flesh afforded a living.

However, this argument really doesn't hold water too well. Many herbivorous lineages, such as the ceratopsians, were at the peak of their diversification and were obviously adjusting very nicely to the change in flora. What then were the really important contributing factors to the wholesale dinosaur extinction?

Perhaps world temperatures were sufficiently altered to affect the ability of dinosaurs to reproduce themselves efficiently. That would certainly be a factor of tremendous consequence. We really have no evidence for any sudden onset of either colder or warmer climates—but even a few degrees change in environmental temperatures would severely affect reptilian physiological processes. Wholly dependent on outside temperatures as these animals are, even a slight fall in the surrounding warmth might prevent them from attaining optimum internal heat requirements—especially the adult giants, whose bulky bodies would take a long time to absorb heat from the sun. Particularly if the climatic changes were of a nature that produced cold nights as contrasted to hot days, getting warm enough again in the morning to do an honest day's business of feeding, mating, and egg laying might become more and more difficult. Then, too, we must bear in mind that excess heat can affect a reptile even more drastically than cold. Reptiles will die of heatstroke at temperatures only slightly above those at which they operate most efficiently. Moreover, those processes most important to the survival of a species, namely the production of eggs and sperm, are badly inhibited at raised temperatures that do not otherwise affect the body but do produce sterility. It is conceivable that, although there were really no drastic changes in world climates, even a slight trend away from previously prevailing world-wide tropical conditions to more temperate ones would produce not only excess cold but also excess heat. For it is a fact that the temperate regions of the world differ from the tropical ones not in being necessarily less warm but rather in showing greater seasonal and daily differences. The nights are usually colder, the days are hotter, and autumn and winter become more marked in their contrast to spring and summer temperatures. A combination of cold nights and seasons, making it difficult for the large forms to attain optimal operating temperatures, together with relatively hotter days and seasons during which the massive animals (if the hot spells lasted sufficiently long) as well as the small forms would be in danger of absorbing too much heat, might be sufficient to account for the extinction of reptiles on a large scale.

Still these are really nothing but undemonstrated theories, since we have no real proof of any climatic change toward the end of the Cretaceous. Even if more variable temperatures did become established in the temperate regions of the world, it is hard to understand why some of the dinosaurs were not able to survive in the equatorial belt where tropical conditions certainly kept on prevailing. After all, the crocodilians — a closely related archosaur stock — did pull through quite successfully to remain as dominant and large reptiles in today's tropics and subtropics.

It used to be thought that the mammals "ousted" the dinosaurs. This theory can definitely be dismissed, since true mammals were around from the early part of the Mesozoic on. It was only after the extinction of the ruling reptiles that they were able to go through their tremendous radiation.

Some people have proposed a "glandular" hypothesis for dinosaurian extinction. They feel that the gland controlling growth, the **hypophysis,** went out of kilter in the Mesozoic giants and that this caused their eradication. This is a rather naïve theory which is discounted by present-day scientists. Size increase must have been an advantage during the equable temperature conditions prevailing during the Mesozoic, since — although there were many small dinosaurs — this latter group in general was characterized by a preponderance of giants. There is an advantage to being large — especially for reptiles. Not only is size a measure of protection, but since the ratio of surface area to mass decreases as size increases, a large animal has relatively less skin surface to absorb heat and radiate heat. Consequently the large animal requires less food in proportion to its size than does the small animal. (A small bird, for example, has to eat constantly in order to keep itself alive.) Particularly for a reptile, with a low rate of metabolism and a fluctuating body temperature, large size would be greatly advantageous and would be selected for under the conditions prevailing during

the Mesozoic Era. Giantism among dinosaurs, rather than being a sign of degeneration and "old age", as has been proposed, was rather a feature of their successful adaptation to the environment.

Then, near the close of the Mesozoic, environmental changes began to take place. There were changes in topography, vegetation, and, conceivably, in world climates. We might have expected the dinosaurs to adapt to these events which, although rapid, geologically speaking, extended over millions of years. Whatever the reasons, they failed to do so and they became extinct.

Why the marine reptiles also vanished at the end of the Cretaceous is an even more difficult problem to solve. Slight variations in air temperatures would not affect the waters of the oceans at all. As we have seen, the ichthyosaurs were already on the way out before the close of the Cretaceous, but what about the plesiosaurs and mosasaurs, both very flourishing groups? Conceivably, competition from the just then rapidly expanding teleost fishes might have been a factor. The demise of the ammonoids, too, if these were an important dietary item, would be a contributing event.

Even if not solving anything, the foregoing discussion should have brought out an appreciation of the highly complex interrelated factors that influence the historical events that are evolution. When we consider extinction, it is always impossible to blame a single factor. Why certain lineages do manage to come up with proper genetic variations which permit adaptation to changes in the environment, and why other lines do not do so and therefore become extinct, cannot be answered simply. What is an obvious conclusion, however, is that evolution is a continuous process constantly striving to populate the earth to its maximum extent. Who and what the actual forms are which dominate at any given period is, from the point of view of the evolutionary process, quite immaterial.

With the extinction of most of the Mesozoic reptiles, the mammals—who until then were being "held back"— were able to become supreme and to fill the land, and to some extent the sea and air, with their representatives. Once more the scene has shifted in the great drama that is evolution—the players are different but their roles are the same. The actors might be somewhat better equipped to read their lines well, under the new conditions, but the play is still about how to make a living.

THE MAMMALS INHERIT THE EARTH

The Mesozoic mammals that lived in the shadow of the dinosaurs were all small, comparatively insignificant creatures. As we have seen, certain of the mammal-like reptiles had reached an evolutionary level in Triassic times at which it is a matter of definition, based on a very few characteristics, as to whether they should be classed with the reptiles or called ancestral mammals. In any case, it was but a very short step from these animals to the first undoubted mammals. By Jurassic times the threshold had unequivocally been crossed from reptile to mammal, and four distinct orders of mammals are known from Jurassic deposits in Europe and North America. Of these, two groups in particular are of interest—the **multituberculates** and the **pantotheres**; the other two—the **triconodonts** and **symmetrodonts**—can be considered "blind alleys" in terms of evolutionary developments beyond the Jurassic.

The multituberculates did not give rise to any of the later mammals and remained until the early Cenozoic a quite separate group of highly specialized animals. They were probably the first herbivorous mammals, to judge from the construction of the heavy skull and their—in some respects—rodent-like dentition (particularly in the development of large gnawing incisors or front teeth). The Cretaceous and early Cenozoic multituberculates showed a tendency towards size increase over their Jurassic forebears, some attaining the size of beavers.

The other important Jurassic group of mammals was the pantotheres. They were small, insignificant-appearing creatures that became extinct by the end of the Jurassic but which, in the particular development of the arrangement and mechanical structure of their teeth, make ideal direct ancestors for all the advanced mammals of Cretaceous and Cenozoic times. Before describing these let us consider the characteristics which dis-

Change of scene.

tinguish mammals as a group from the reptilian level of organization.

The difference in jaw articulation, with the two reptilian articular elements becoming added to the stapes of the middle ear, has already been mentioned. The brain case of mammals is expanded over that of the reptiles, although the early mammals really do not show much advance over the reptilian type of nervous system. However, there is a definite trend for the mammalian brain to become more and more complex, so that throughout their history every line of mammals has shown a progressive increase in intelligence. Learning, or the ability to profit from experience, has played an increasingly important role in the life of mammals, whereas both reptiles and birds are creatures mainly of instinct or stereotyped innate responses. Such reactions are well enough adapted to a particular mode of existence to enable birds as well as reptiles to perform highly intricate actions, but they are not modifiable in the sense that true learning is. Birds have specialized on the instinctive side of behaviour (for example, their complex nest-building activities and courtship rituals), whereas mammals have emphasized the more flexible and adaptable part of the nervous system,

namely those structures of the brain that permit experience to modify behaviour.

Reptiles have scales; mammals have fur. The evolution of hair was closely related to the attainment of a physiological mechanism for keeping body temperatures constant even under fluctuating environmental conditions. This in turn necessitated a generally higher metabolic activity. Food had to be handled as efficiently as possible, and the markedly differentiated teeth of mammals permit optimal chewing and chopping, so that digestion is able to extract every last bit of nutritive value. The circulatory system, too, had to become more efficient in order to handle the large amounts of oxygen now required.

In mammals the amniote egg became modified to being retained within the mother's body in varying degrees. In one line, the **marsupial mammals,** the eggs that are kept inside the body contain only a comparatively small amount of yolk and have no shell around them. The embryos derive some additional nourishment from the mother's blood for a very limited amount of time to be born alive as tiny larval young. These immediately crawl into a special external pouch where they attach themselves to milk glands located on the mother's skin

113

inside the pouch and where they remain for several weeks. Only after this additional period in an external incubator are the young capable of any independence. The other mammalian lineage, the **placental mammals,** have gone a step further in their reproductive modifications. Here the young are born in a comparatively advanced stage of development. The structure which enables the the embryo to derive nourishment from the mother's blood stream, namely the **placenta,** is developed to a much higher degree than in marsupials—the egg being almost yolkless. Placentals have no pouch, and their milk glands are exposed on the surface of the skin. However, both pouched as well as placental mammals are characterized by live birth of their young and by the possession of skin glands which have been modified to furnish milk for their offspring.

The Jurassic pantotheres are felt to be the common ancestors of both placentals and marsupials. It is doubtful that the former ever went through a marsupial stage—rather, both lineages have been independent from the beginning of their evolution which commenced in Cretaceous times.

The American opossum is a practically unchanged Cretaceous marsupial. Marsupials were world-wide in their distribution during Cretaceous and early Cenozoic times. However, except for the surviving opossums in North and South America, Australia is now the only continent inhabited by them. How do we explain this relict survival? Sometime during the Cretaceous, before the arrival of the progressive placentals, Australia became completely separated from the Asiatic mainland, and here the marsupials lived on with virtually no placental competition. Consequently the marsupials enjoyed a wide range of adaptive radiation on this island continent. There are large herbivores—the kangaroos—and many small herbivorous and omnivorous animals—the marsupial "woodchucks" **(wombats),** "mice" and "moles", the pouched "squirrels" **(phalangers),** and other forms—that have their analogous representatives among the placentals. There are large and small marsupial carnivores similar in outward appearance to wolves, cats, and weasels. As we shall see, there was one other continent on which the marsupials enjoyed some success—in South America. However, they were ousted from there towards the end of the Cenozoic.

There live today two animals which we call mammals but which can be assigned neither to the marsupials nor to the placentals. They occur only in Australia and New Guinea and constitute the order of the **monotremes.** These are the **platypus** or duckbill *(Ornithorhynchus)* and the **echidna** or spiny anteater *(Tachyglossus).* Superficially these monotremes are highly specialized. The platypus has a duck-like beak for burrowing in the mud of streams in search of worms and grubs. The anteater has sharp spines and an elongated tubular snout for probing anthills. But basically the recent monotremes are representative of an advanced mammal-like reptile grade of organization. They lay eggs in burrows, but they do suckle their young on milk secreted from modified sweat glands. They have three bones in the middle ear and the mammalian jaw articulation, but in many features of the skull and other parts of the skeleton they show reptilian characteristics. Their body temperatures fluctuate greatly with the environment, and physiologically they are really quite reptilelike. Most scientists feel that the monotremes represent a separate line of descent from the mammal-like reptiles that have continued in an isolated corner of the world.

The basic placental stock is represented by generalized ancestral **insectivores,** such as *Deltatheridium,* found together with Cretaceous dinosaurs in central Asia. Certain generalized insectivores gave rise to all the other orders of placental mammals. These must have begun their essential differentiation well back in the Cretaceous, for at the beginning of the Cenozoic we already find all the major types of placentals in existence. The **shrews,** the **moles,** and the Old-World **hedgehogs** are specialized modern insectivores. In a very loose way we can get some idea of what the ancestral Cretaceous placentals looked like by comparing them to shrews in size, outward appearance, and general behaviour. They must have been small, secretive animals, living mainly on insects varied with worms, grubs, and soft fruits. Scurrying through the underbrush and climbing through the trees, they must have played much the same role in the world of dinosaurs as their modern insectivore descendants play among the other more impressive placental groups. However, some of them developed lines of descent that led

One of the first placental mammals; *Deltatheridium,* an insectivore from the Cretaceous period.

to all our familiar modern mammals, including ourselves.

This tremendous evolutionary burst occurred during the Cenozoic Era, which has consequently been called the **Age of Mammals.** This last phase of the earth's history began about 70 million years ago and is divided into a Tertiary period of considerable magnitude and a second period, the Quaternary, barely begun a million years ago. The Tertiary is considered to be of 69 million years' duration and is divided into five epochs: **Paleocene** (15 million years long), **Eocene** (19 million years), **Oligocene** (10 million years), **Miocene** (15 million years), and **Pliocene** (10 million years). The Quaternary includes only the short **Pleistocene** epoch (under a million years) and **Recent** times.

The Mesozoic-Cenozoic transition was a time of continental uplift. The shallow seas characteristic of the middle to late Mesozoic receded from the land, and the modern mountain systems were born: the Alps and Himalayas of the Old World, and the Rockies and Andes of the New. The Cenozoic marked the beginning of a long period of mountain making that, with intervening periods of rest and consequent erosion, is actively continuing at the present day. Climatic zones first became established with the onset of Cenozoic times, and the alternation of seasons became more marked, especially in the higher latitudes. These changes took place gradually during the course of the Age of Mammals.

Early Tertiary times are characterized by a generally warm, equable climate which slowly gave place to the extreme climatic conditions of the Pleistocene. This last epoch is often called the **Great Ice Age,** since it includes four glacial periods during which vast tracts of the earth lay barren like so many enormous, white, lifeless deserts of ice. The Recent —or **Holocene**—began towards the close of the fourth great period of frost, some ten to fifteen thousand years ago, and is, according to many scientists, merely an interglacial period corresponding to the other three warmer intervals between the four Pleistocene glacial periods.

To anyone from the Cretaceous, it was a different world that followed the close of the Mesozoic. It was now the Paleocene, the first epoch of Cenozoic times. The colossal ruling reptiles had disappeared, and of their mighty dynasty only turtles, lizards, constrictors, and crocodiles survived. The aspect of the Paleocene fauna was mainly a mammalian one, but of a strange and unfamiliar kind. Many of the mammals then present are assigned to still existing orders—such as insectivores, carnivores, and primates. But these Paleocene representatives were for the most part small archaic and aberrant types, and much of the fauna belonged to orders now entirely extinct.

The few mammalian forms known from the Cretaceous were still present. There were opossum-like marsupials, such as *Thylacodon*. The multituberculates (of Jurassic origin) were very abundant —most of them were small, but *Taeniolabis* and its allies were beaver-sized animals. The insectivores had already split up into various specialized lineages —there were primitive hedgehogs like *Prodiacodon* and early tenrecs such as *Paleoryctes*. The Paleocene fauna also contained a short-lived outgrowth from the primitive insectivore stock—the herbivorous **taeniodonts,** of which *Psittacotherium* is an early Paleocene representative.

The Paleocene epoch after the extinction of the dinosaurs. Bottom row from right to left: *Loxolophus*— a small primitive creodont. *Palaeophis*—a primitive snake belonging to the boa family. *Prodiacodon*—

V. Hancke

a primitive insectivore related to present-day hedgehogs. *Thylacodon*—primitive opossum-like marsupial. *Taeniolabis*—a multituberculate—the size of a woodchuck. *Palaeoryctes*—small insectivores—related to tenrecs. Above from left to right: A swamp-dwelling turtle. *Tetraclaenodon*—a condylarth—the group that gave rise to the hoofed mammals. *Plesiadapis*—an early primate belonging to the lemur group. A crocodile.

Among the most prominent placentals were the early carnivores, the stem **creodonts**—many of them weasel-sized creatures, of which *Loxolophus* is an example. However, some of these were as large as small bears. In their teeth they show the beginnings of the specialized shearing and cutting dentition so characteristic of later carnivores (such as dogs and cats). They preyed on the primitive **ungulates** (or hoofed animals), the **condylarths.** These looked nothing like the sort of creature we have in mind when we think of a hoofed animal. Rather they were small, cat-sized herbivores with teeth still resembling those of insectivores and with clawed feet. There were a number of different families of condylarths present in the Paleocene, among which the group that contained *Tetraclaenodon* appears to be the one that gave rise to the more advanced ungulate orders. The **pantodonts** (also called **amblypods**) were an aberrant group of hoofed mammals that produced relatively large forms such as sheep-sized *Pantolambda* and the four-foot-high, massive genus *Barylambda*. These bulky animals were probably rather difficult prey for the early creodonts to pull down.

The primates, the order to which the lemurs, the monkeys, the apes, and humans belong, appeared in middle Paleocene times. They were tree-shrew-like creatures, long-tailed forms, transitional between insectivores and lemurs. One of these was *Plesiadapis*. Many of them showed odd specializations in their dentition, developing rodent-like incisor.

There are also isolated finds of fully developed ancestral rodents and ancestral hares. The rabbits and hares are not rodents but comprise the order of **lagomorphs,** which has run parallel to that of the rodents in many of its evolutionary developments. The most characteristic features of both rodents and lagomorphs are their adaptations for gnawing: the strong, constantly growing chisel-

Large hoofed animals of the final phase of the Paleocene epoch. Sheep-sized *Pantolambda* in front, and four-foot-high *Barylambda* behind. Both are amblypods, or pantodonts, an early and now extinct order of ungulates.

like incisors and the highly specialized jaw musculature used in activating these gnawing tools.

The Paleocene fauna included a large number of modern birds, very similar to the forms we know today. The toothed birds had all died out by the end of the Cretaceous.

In many respects the Paleocene record gives us some tantalizing glimpses of early placental deployment, but unfortunately it is too incomplete to include enough of the truly transitional forms. Many of the mammalian orders were in existence and had already undergone a fair degree of adaptive radiation. However, most of the specialized forms pro-duced in this first branching out of the placentals were soon to be replaced by the descendants of more generalized, related types. This second wave of placental radiation, including the direct ancestors of many of the modern mammals, did not really get under way until the end of the next epoch, the Eocene.

The Eocene epoch brought with it approximately twenty million years of mild and damp climate. The greater part of the earth was covered by subtropical jungle, and natural conditions favoured the development of the mammals who —to an ever increasing extent—were filling all the ecological niches left va-

Hoofed animals of the Eocene epoch. On the right, *Uintatherium,* and drinking in the background, closely related *Eobasileus;* both are dinoceratids, a now extinct order of early ungulates. On the bottom left, *Phenacodus,* a condylarth. Above it, *Coryphodon,* a pantodont.

cant by the dinosaurs.

Most of the Eocene was still marked by the presence of archaic types of placental mammals carried over from the Paleocene epoch. Toward its end, however, the ancestors of the modern mammals put in their appearance and quickly replaced their related predecessors. The vegetation of Eocene times was already very much like that of recent times, but the mammals were still in the melting pot, so to speak.

Many hoofed animals of Paleocene origin retained their position as the giants of their time. The amblypods were represented by clumsy creatures such as *Coryphodon,* of tapir size and habits. A distantly related early ungulate division comprising the *Dinocerata* (also of Paleocene origin) culminated in late Eocene times with bizarre forms like *Eobasileus* and *Uintatherium,* peculiarly horned animals about the size of modern rhinoceroses. Neither of them survived the Eocene epoch.

The most interesting of the condylarths, however, was *Phenacodus,* of late Paleocene and early Eocene times, for it is generalized enough in its anatomical features to be representative of the type of creature that gave rise to all the various orders of hoofed mammals. *Phenacodus* itself is much too late in time to be the actual ancestral form, but it is probably a relatively little modified descendant of such a stem ungulate. *Phenacodus* (probably derived from the group to which the Paleocene *Tetraclaenodon* belonged) was a sheep-sized animal, resembling in many respects some sort of primitive carnivore more than it did an ungulate. It had a long, low skull; its limbs were short and heavy, and the feet were short with all the toes present. However, although its canines were large, the cheek teeth formed a continuous series and the molars had the square crowns (for grinding up plant food) characteristic of all the later hoofed mammals. Its toes, instead of ending in claws, terminated in small hoofs. All in all, the condylarth *Phenacodus* makes a very suitable stem ungulate, and it must have been a relatively clumsy forest- or prairie-dwelling herbivore.

The creodonts or early carnivores were very well represented in Eocene times on the Eurasian as well as the North American continent. There was *Andrewsarchus* from Mongolia, a true giant with a skull three feet in length (*Sarkastodon* was a related contemporary genus). The North American genus *Patriofelis,* of tiger size, represented another creodont lineage. *Mesonyx* of North America belonged to the same group as did the later *Andrewsarchus.* There were, from Paleocene times on, several different lines of evolution among these early carnivores. They can be distinguished by differences in the appearance and arrangement of their teeth. All of them developed **carnassials,** that is, sharp cutting teeth derived from modified molars. The exact type of modification and the particular position in the jaw of the molars so adapted varied from lineage to lineage. However, in overall appearance and diversification, the three groups paralleled one another fairly closely—with small, medium-sized, and large types occurring in each. All these creodont lines became extinct at the end of the Eocene except one, the **hyaenodonts,** which continued all through the Oligocene and Miocene to die out at the beginning of the Pliocene epoch. However, there was present—from Paleo-

Eurasian creodonts, or early carnivores. On the left, *Andrewsarchus; Sarkastodon* is on the right, and above it is weasel-sized *Miacis,* belonging to the group that gave rise to all the modern carnivores.

cene times on—one group of creodonts, the **miacids,** which, although becoming extinct at the end of the Eocene (like most of the early carnivores), showed certain progressive features, such as the relatively high development of their brain and the anterior position of their carnassials, which make them the logical ancestors of all the modern carnivores. These last, the **fissipeds,** comprise the **canoids** (dogs, bears, raccoons, and weasels) and the **feloids** (civets, hyenas, and cats).

The miacids were small, early Tertiary carnivores of weasel-like appearance, quite abundant in both Eurasia and

North American creodonts. Two individuals belonging to the genus *Mesonyx; Patriofelis* is crouching on the rocks.

North America during Eocene times. They were probably forest dwellers, preying on small rodents that were by now fairly common.

One of the most interesting features of the Eocene epoch is that it marks the first appearance of the dominant ungulates of later Tertiary times: the **perissodactyls** ("odd-toed" hoofed forms such as the horses, tapirs, and rhinoceroses) and the "even-toed" **artiodactyls** (such as pigs, hippopotamuses, camels, deer, sheep, and cattle).

The perissodactyls are ungulates in which the weight-bearing axis of the foot passes through the middle toe. In all of them the inner toe (the thumb in the fore foot and large toe in the hind foot) has disappeared together with the fifth digit in the hind foot. (That makes four toes for the front and three for the rear.) In most of them the fifth digit in the fore foot has also disappeared, leaving three functional toes in each foot, in all except the most primitive perissodactyls. One lineage, the one leading to modern horses, has reduced even this limited number to only one functional toe—the middle one—in each foot.

One of the first horses (really just generalized perissodactyls at this point) was *Hyracotherium,* better but incorrectly known as *Eohippus,* and found in both Eurasia and North America. With the close of the Eocene, *Hyracotherium* became extinct in the Old World, and from then on the evolution of horses was limited to the North American continent. All the horses that appeared later in Eurasia, Africa, and South America were emigrants from North America.

The Eocene genus *Hyrachyus* of North America was the earliest rhinoceros, not quite as small as *Eohippus,* with slender limbs and long feet, without horns on its skull. It looked anything but like a present-day rhinoceros. *Hyracotherium* did not look like a modern horse either. It was a small forest animal about the size of a fox, lightly built, with limbs clearly adapted for running. It had a slightly curved back; there were four toes in the front foot and three toes in the hind limb. As a generalization, it might be said that small size was a characteristic of the oldest forebears of all the big hoofed animals of our day.

The middle Eocene genus *Palaeosyops* was a modestly sized representative of the later-to-become-gigantic **titanotheres,** a perissodactyl group that became extinct during the Oligocene.

The artiodactyls which first appear fully fledged (and quite distinct from the perissodactyls) in the Eocene were also small creatures. In artiodactyls the axis of the foot (bearing most of the weight of the body) passes between the third and fourth digits. They have either two or four toes in each foot—the first digit almost never being present. The first artiodactyls looked superficially much like the creodonts that preyed on them. Among the most primitive are the early swine, but all the various lineages leading to hippopotamuses, camels, and others were already established by late Eocene times. For example. *Protylophus,* a cat-sized creature with short limbs, was an ancestral camel.

Late in the Eocene epoch there lived in Egypt a very interesting hoofed animal. It was *Moeritherium,* the first **proboscidean**—the group to which the living elephants and extinct mastodons as well as other now extinct groups belong. It was no bigger than a fully grown pig and had neither tusks nor a trunk. However, there were indications of both—particularly of the former in a noticeable enlargement of the second upper and lower incisors (front teeth), which in later descendants became imposing ivory lances.

While the newly arrived hoofed animals were gradually replacing the primitive condylarths, the primates

Moeritherium, the first proboscidean known from the fossil record.

were consolidating their kingdom in the treetops.

In addition to the somewhat specialized primitive types still hanging on from Paleocene times, there were true **lemurs** and **tarsiers** much as we find them living today in tropical parts of the Old World. The lemur *Notharctus*, for example, is known from complete skeletons discovered in North America. It was a climbing animal with "opposable" thumbs and large toes that enabled it to grasp branches with hands and feet as it clambered among the treetops.

The Eocene tarsier *Tetonius* is a New World form already highly specialized for the nocturnal type of existence that the single living genus *Tarsius* exemplifies today. *Tetonius* had enormous orbits (the cavities in the skull containing the eyes), so that we can conclude that sight was the most important of its senses. Tarsiers have short muzzles and forwardly placed eyes, and at one time they were thought to be transitional between the lemurs and the true monkeys which represent the next higher step in primate evolution. How-

Small animals with proud descendants. From the left: *Protylopus*—one of the first camels. *Lambdotherium*—a small early titanothere. *Hyrachyus*—one of the earliest rhinoceroses. *Eohippus* (also called *Hyracotherium*)—two "dawn horses" are drinking.

New World Eocene prosimians, or primitive primates. Above: *Tetonius,* a big-eyed tarsier. Below: *Notharctus,* a lemur.

ever, it is now generally felt that the tarsiers are a specialized side branch paralleling certain advanced primate developments rather than being true connecting links.

No traces of true monkeys are found from before the Oligocene, but that, of course, does not mean they were not around before then. The arboreal habits of primates make them notoriously poor items in all fossil collections. If we can judge from the rather scanty evidence, primates disappeared from North America shortly after the Eocene, and most of their evolution up to the human level occurred in the Old World. It is unfortunate that although we have some good fossils indicating man's close relationship to the **apes** (with whom we share a common ancestry), in general our own evolution is one of the least documented among mammals.

Monkeys, apes, and men together comprise the **anthropoids,** or advanced primates. This grouping can in turn be subdivided into the **New World monkeys,** the **Old World monkeys,** and finally the **hominoids** (apes and men). All of the anthropoids can sit upright, leaving the hands free for manipulating objects. The thumb and great toe are generally set apart from the other digits (as in the lemurs and tarsiers), but in many anthropoids this feature has become highly perfected. In all of them the muzzle has retreated and the eyes are placed far forward, permitting simultaneous use of both. Only when the two eyes are thus focused together does depth perception, or stereoscopic vision, become possible. The perfection of vision has played a tremendous role in the evolution of the primate brain and is closely tied up with the remarkable degree of intelligence shown by all the anthropoids. Increase in brain size has characterized the evolution of all the mammalian orders, but in primates the enormous expansion of the **cerebral hemispheres**—permitting complex memory associations and detailed interpretation of visual stimuli in particular—has been the single most important factor in their success. But we shall have to leave the rest of this story, in which man is the hero of one particular evolutionary episode, to future chapters.

Early in the Tertiary period (probably during the Paleocene) an event took place which was to have remarkable consequences. The sea washed over the Panama isthmus and severed the previously existing connection between North and South America; so that, while North America and Eurasia appear to have been almost continuously connected with periodic severance by occasional submergence of the Bering land bridge, South America was an isolated continent from the beginning of the Tertiary until its close. The Panama isthmus was re-established during the Tertiary-Quaternary transition. Now a very interesting situation developed in South America during the period of its isolation. The early condylarths that had moved into South America before its separation from North America developed their own peculiar and independent evolutionary lineages. Instead of artiodactyls, perissodactyls, and proboscideans we find other orders of herbivorous mammals (such as the **notoungulates**) which in many of their developments paralleled the hoofed mammals of the north. The reduction of digits in the foot followed along lines similar to perissodactyl and artiodactyl trends, and there were South American forms that vaguely resembled "horses", "rhinoceroses", "tapirs", "camels", and even "proboscideans", or crosses between several of these.

South American ecological niches, in addition to these peculiar ungulates, were also filled by the **edentates**—the armadillos, anteaters, and sloths. The early edentates, although originally present in North America, became extinct on that continent but were able to develop successful descendants in the isolated situation provided by South America.

That takes care of the herbivores, but what about carnivores? Here, too, we encounter an unusual situation. Apparently the primitive placental carnivores, the creodonts, never penetrated South America before its isolation; however, the marsupials did, and from primitive opossum-like forms there developed aggressive carnivores which in their development converged towards northern creodonts and later carnivores to a remarkable extent. These marsupial "dogs" and "cats" were the **borhyaenids,** and they preyed on the placental notoungulates and edentates, as well as on certain rodent-like marsupials that had also evolved in South America. As we shall see later, when the Panama land bridge became re-established at the end of the Tertiary period, with a concomitant placental invasion of advanced artiodactyls, perissodactyls, and fissiped carnivores, most of the distinct South American fauna, until then highly successful, was literally "dispossessed" and became extinct. A similar situation is occurring today in Australia. With the coming of white colonists to that island continent many placentals were introduced; for example, dogs, foxes, sheep, rabbits, and rodents. Marsupials apparently are no match for placental mammals, and Australia's distinctive fauna is rapidly disappearing.

As the reptiles had done before them, the land mammals also sent their representatives back to life's first primitive home, the sea. The first placentals must have taken to the oceans during the Paleocene epoch, for the Eocene seas already housed both highly specialized sea cows **(sirenians)** as well as fully fledged large whales **(cetaceans)**. As would be expected from ocean-going animals, they were even then widely distributed throughout the world. The whales (including the porpoises) have shown an almost incredible convergence towards the appearance of fishes and also of the reptilian ichthyosaurs. Faced with similar adaptive problems, selection has picked those mutations which have tended to produce similar phenotypic results, although the initial basic material was different in each case.

The exact ancestry of the whales is completely unknown, but they are clearly descended from land-living placentals. By upper Eocene times we already encounter giant forms like *Basilosaurus,* sixty feet long. All the early cetaceans had a relatively primitive skull with teeth, but by Miocene times two distinct lineages had developed. One is that of the **toothed whales** (porpoises, sperm whales, and others), and the other includes the **whalebone whales** (such as the titanic blue whales — 100 feet in length and weighing 150 tons). In these last, the teeth are suppressed and transverse fibrous plates, hanging from the roof of the mouth, strain small animals from the water.

The sirenians (sea cows or manatees) are classified as ungulates modified for an aquatic mode of life along sea coasts and in rivers that flow into the sea. They are herbivores that feed on underwater vegetation. In certain of their features, particularly in the dentition, they appear to be distantly related to the stem forms that gave rise to the proboscideans.

The Eocene also marks the first appearance of the **bats,** a separate order of placentals clearly derived from an insectivore stock but highly specialized for an aerial way of life. Bats are the only mammals capable of true flight. In many of their adaptations they can be compared to the long-extinct pterosaurs. As in flying reptiles, the forelimb of bats has become modified to support a wing membrane, except that all the fingers, and not just the fourth, are elongated for this purpose. This is really "better", for a tear in the multiple-ribbed bat wing would not be nearly as disastrous as a rip through the singly supported pterosaur structure. The bats are nocturnal animals, not really in active competition with the mostly diurnal birds. Most of them are insect eaters, but some are fruit-eating forms. They rely mainly on their wonderfully acute sense of hearing to avoid obstacles and to locate food in the dark, using a system that can be compared to sonar — the twentieth-century echo-location system developed just a decade or so ago. Bats, because of their habits, are — like birds and, to some extent, tree-dwelling primates — rarely covered with sediments and therefore not usually found preserved. Although our first record is from the Eocene, they must certainly have diverged much earlier than that from an insectivore ancestry, since the Eocene bats are highly developed and show little difference from their modern relatives.

Primitive rodents, some of which first appeared in the Paleocene, had become fairly numerous and diversified by Eocene times, particularly in North America, although they also occurred in Europe and Asia. In addition to some of the primitive types, among which the sewellel or "mountain beaver" of the Pacific Northwest is a sole survivor, there were also true pocket gophers and forms related to the living kangaroo rats of the Southwest deserts. Ancestral squirrels and woodchucks have also been found in Eocene deposits. It seems that the mouse family (including rats and voles) and the porcupine assemblage (which includes the valuable chinchilla, by the way) were comparative late-comers which can be traced back only as far as the Oligocene.

Some of the Eocene flightless running birds with secondarily reduced wings, such as *Diatryma* of North America, must have been active carnivores preying on the primitive ungulates of the time, if we are to judge character from their impressive size and recurved ripping beak.

As the Eocene drew towards its close, animal life was beginning to change character. Apart from the isolated situations offered by Australia and South America, only a few of the archaic mammals (the various condylarths and creodonts) survived in competition with the advance guard of the modern mammals—the initial radiation of the perissodactyls, artiodactyls, proboscideans, and fissiped carnivores.

Mammals take to the sea. In the background are two Eocene whales *(Zeuglodon)*, and in front, two early sea cows or manatees *(Protosiren)*.

THE GOLDEN AGE OF MAMMALS

During Oligocene and Miocene times climates became cooler and the old subtropical forests of North America, Europe, and central Asia were pushed southward to warmer climes, leaving the temperate zone to the hardier conifers and deciduous trees. When this temperate trend continued during the whole of the Miocene epoch, the great forest regions were gradually converted into open plains. The **grasses,** which up to now had played a relatively minor role among the· flora of the Earth, spread themselves as a golden carpet of cereals across the sun-drenched open prairies.

The spread of the plains grasses was an important event—the steppes of Europe and Asia, the veldt of South Africa, and North America's prairies stem from that time. The new environments provided by the rise of the savannahs of the world were tremendously important influences on future evolutionary developments.

The grasses provided a source of abundant, concentrated food. But to take advantage of this required changes in the dentition of animals that had been accustomed to browsing on soft green vegetation. Teeth had to become tougher and had to last longer if the harsh plains grasses were to become a steady food item. Consequently, the ungulates that came out of the forests developed heavily ridged teeth that grew almost as fast as

they were worn down. The ancestral horses, cattle, antelopes, and camels that left the swamps and forests not only became highly adapted in their dentition, but they developed into longer-footed, swifter-running forms on the hard-soiled open prairies. Padded feet and small hoofs gave way to springy limbs and larger hoofs. The tapirs, rhinos, titanotheres, piglike artiodactyls, and proboscideans stayed on in the forests—they became rarer, migrated, or changed their habits as the forests dwindled and retreated. To the plains also came the newly developed fissipeds—the dog-wolves and swift-running cats with limbs adapted to catch the galloping herbivores.

Australia and South America remained isolated as before, but contact between North America, Eurasia, and Africa was relatively well maintained via an alternately wet and dry Bering land bridge and across the Mediterranean, then much restricted.

The plains, as well as the forests, were filled with a tremendous variety of hoofed animals. However, many of these prominent members of the middle Tertiary fauna became extinct after a relatively brief span of glory.

The titanotheres were among the largest animals of the Oligocene—and many of these perissodactyls were veritable giants. Spreading out from

An odd scene. During the Eocene, giant flightless birds such as *Diatryma* probably preyed on the primitive perissodactyls which gave rise to horses and rhinoceroses.

North America, they invaded Asia in early Oligocene times and a few got as far west as Europe. Most of them were advanced horned forms—such as fifteen foot-long *Brontops*. However, during the middle of the Oligocene the group became extinct. One of the reasons given for its demise is that the titanotheres were "unable" to adapt their dentition to the harsh plains grasses, since the cheek teeth, throughout titanothere history, had remained low crowned and adequate only for the soft vegetation of early Tertiary times. But, of course, this theory does not explain why the titanotheres could not stay on in the remaining forests as did the tapirs and others.

Among the artiodactyls, the **entelodonts,** a piglike group (but not true pigs at all), showed an early trend towards large size. During Oligocene times some became as large as boars, and the early Miocene genus *Dinohyus* attained bison size. The skull in these North American entelodonts was over a yard long, but the brain was relatively small compared to the true pigs and peccaries that had appeared by the early Oligocene. (Pigs and peccaries are closely related, but the former are an Old World lineage, whereas the peccaries evolved, in a parallel fashion to pigs, in North America.) The entelodonts became extinct over the whole northern hemisphere during the Miocene, probably being replaced by the more intelligent pigs and peccaries of the Old and New Worlds respectively.

Among the South American notoungulates the **toxodonts** were a group that

Oligocene titanotheres (*Brontops*), in flight during a volcanic eruption.

roughly paralleled the rhinoceroses of other continental areas. *Nesodon,* of Miocene age, had a deep skull and short, broad feet with three functional toes, the axis of the foot passing through the middle toe. Such an arrangement is similar in function but not in origin to the feet of rhinos. Toxodonts were a successful notoungulate group during late Eocene, Oligocene, and Miocene times, declining after that. They continued into the Pleistocene before becoming extinct. In one group of toxodonts the toes ended in claws rather than hoofs—a development which can be compared to that of certain contemporary clawed perissodactyls of the northern hemisphere.

These last, the **chalicotheres,** never a numerous clan, are now extinct. They were closely related to the titanotheres. Their stem forms had appeared by upper Eocene times, and they evolved rapidly in both Eurasia and North America throughout the Oligocene and early Miocene. Later Pliocene and Pleistocene representatives looked

very much like the Miocene genus *Moropus.* This was a horselike form in some respects—such as in size and in the appearance of its long, deep face, compact body, and elongated limbs. But here the resemblance ended, for *Moropus* had low crowned teeth like the titanotheres and its front legs were longer than the hind limbs, giving it a sloping back. But the oddest thing about it was

Miocene South American toxodonts (*Nesodon*).

130

its short feet with claws instead of hoofs on all the three functional toes. It looks as though the chalicotheres were adapted for browsing off high-growing vegetation, possibly using their claws to dig into the soil and tree trunk while rearing up to get at a juicy branch. Whatever their mode of life, they can be considered a restricted but successful group since they continued well into the Pleistocene, becoming extinct during the Ice Age together with many of the large mammals of those times.

Among the "blind alleys" of Tertiary times can be numbered the **oreodonts**—a strictly North American artiodactyl group. They are not clearly related to any other "even-toed" assemblage and seem to stand somewhere between the pigs and hippopotamuses on the one side and the camels and the ruminants (or cud-chewing artiodactyls) on the other. They appeared in late Eocene times and were extremely successful until the beginning of the Miocene, when they declined in numbers due to competition from the rapidly spreading advanced ruminants. (The last few oreodont stragglers became extinct during the Pliocene.) They ranged in size from small animals to beasts comparable in size to very large pigs. Generally their body was long with short limbs—some may have been arboreal (these had claws instead of hoofs); others were sheeplike, and a third line went in for amphibious, hippopotamus-like habits.

Some of the early ruminants looked very much like their modern, little-changed descendants, the Oriental **chevrotains** or "mouse deer", forms no bigger than jack rabbits. These primitive ruminants (they are not true deer) are called **traguloids,** and their main line of

Moropus—a Miocene chalicothere. This was a perissodactyl which looked like a cross between a horse, a bear, and a camel, with long claws on its feet.

development (from the Eocene on) leading to the Old World chevrotains was in Eurasia, but during the middle and late Tertiary they developed some interesting side branches (now extinct) that evolved in North America. One of these were the **protoceratids,** represented by the Oligocene *Protoceras,* the Miocene *Syndyoceras,* and the Pliocene *Synthetoceras.* There was a trend towards size increase among these deerlike ruminants—their last Pliocene representatives being as big as modern deer. However, their most striking feature was the really weird assortment of horns sported by the males. *Protoceras* had six horns—two on the nose, two over the eyes, and a third pair on the back of its head. In *Syndyoceras* there were only two pairs of horns—one above the eyes and the second consisting of two long diverging horns on the nose. The culminating Pliocene genus *Synthetoceras* had backwardly directed horns over its eyes, and on its nose there was a single Y-shaped outgrowth—longer than the total length of the skull.

Now let us consider the evolutionary development of the various groups of hoofed animals that have well-known representatives among us today: the horses, rhinos, and tapirs, all perissodactyls, and the artiodactyls represented by pigs and hippopotamuses and by camels, as well as by the advanced ruminants, such as deer, sheep, antelopes, and cattle.

As mentioned previously, the Eurasian line of early horses died out with the close of the Eocene, and horse evolution became limited to North America where a number of interesting trends can be followed in great detail. Now one of the outstanding examples used in past times to illustrate "straight-line" evolution has been the development of the horse. As must already be clear from much that has been discussed before, such **orthogenesis** does not occur. No lineage follows a straight path from,

say, small to large size. There are always numerous side branches showing varying degrees of "progressive" and "conservative" features. This same applies to the story of the horse. It is true that the particular line leading from *Hyracotherium* to modern *Equus* is marked by a progressive size increase, lengthening of the feet, reduction of side toes, and increase in the height of the crowns of the cheek teeth, but when the horses are considered as a group in all their ramified, branching history, no such picture of uniform evolution becomes apparent. At the beginning of their North American history, the horses followed a fairly direct trend leading up to the Oligocene genus *Miohippus*. All the progressive features mentioned above were well marked in this line, *Miohippus* being sheep-sized, with three functional toes on each foot—the middle toe being the longest. However, the teeth were still low-crowned. From this stage horse evolution branched out

In the foreground are two individuals of the genus Metamynodon — an Oligocene water-loving rhinoceros. To the left, above, is Protoceras — a primitive ruminant related to modern deer.

considerably. Some lines remained conservative and stayed more or less at the *Miohippus* level. These were small browsers on relatively soft vegetation. Another line of horses increased in size so that by the end of the Miocene they were almost as large as modern horses, but they retained low-crowned teeth and functional three-toed feet. These were probably forest dwellers (much like deer today). Some of them spread into the Old World where they became very common. The line to which *Equus* belongs was continued during Miocene times by *Merychippus*. This was a horse as large as a small pony, still with three-toed feet, but the middle toe had become the only functional one. *Merychippus* walked on the single middle toe, the end of which was enclosed in a large hoof. The teeth had become definitely high-crowned with an intricately folded and partially cemented surface for efficient grinding up of hard plant fibres and seeds. *Merychippus*, then, was a plains dweller and already highly adapted for its particular way of life. It was from a *Merychippus* ancestry that *Equus* eventually developed, but as we shall see, the line leading to the modern horse was but one of several—the rest having become extinct.

The rhinoceroses, derived from an Eocene stock quite similar to that of the horses, developed running forms that paralleled in their adaptations some of the early contemporaneous equids. Already present in late Eocene times was another branch of rhinos which developed amphibious habits. These were large, heavy animals with stocky limbs; *Metamynodon* of the Oligocene is an example. They were successful for a time, spreading from North America into Asia and Europe, but they became extinct soon after the Oligocene. The central stock of rhinoceros evolution arose from some of the running rhinos. By Oligocene times there already existed massive representatives, five feet high, with the broad three-toed feet and grinding cheek teeth characteristic of modern forms. Some lines developed horns; others remained hornless. (The outgrowths on the skull of rhinos are not true horns but consist of coalesced hair.) One hornless group, of which the late Oligocene to early Miocene genus *Baluchitherium* from Mongolia is a primary example, developed into giants eighteen feet high at the shoulders.

Primitive tapirs appeared in Eocene times, and they can be compared to the early perissodactyls that gave rise to horses and rhinos. To this day the modern tapirs of South America and Malaya, remnants of a once world-wide group, retain the four front toes and three hind toes of their Eocene ancestors. From their beginnings tapirs have remained forest dwellers adapted to moving on soft, swampy terrain rather than hard soil. By Oligocene times true tapirs occurred in both Europe and North America—*Protapirus* was a characteristic genus, little different from modern forms. It already had, at least to some degree, a very flexible nose. This short proboscis serves as a tool to be wrapped around plant stems while browsing.

Among living artiodactyls the hippopotamuses are perhaps the most closely related to the pigs and peccaries. Most pigs, from Oligocene times on, have been—in spite of their variety—creatures of essentially similar habits—forest animals rooting in the ground for

A primitive tapir with its young *(Protapirus)*. In the background, *Bothriodon*, an anthracothere, the group believed to have given rise to the hippopotamuses.

from some of the later anthracotheres.

Although camels chew the cud like the ruminants, they have had a long, separate history from the rest of the cud-chewing artiodactyls. The North American Eocene camels (vaguely resembling some of the early oreodonts) were already distinct from the first true ruminants—the traguloids. Throughout Cenozoic history most of them increased in size to become medium-sized or even giant artiodactyls. The Miocene *Alticamelus* raised its head ten feet above the ground, but there were other lightly built gazelle-like camels present. In general, the legs became elongated and the neck increased in length. In the later Tertiary camels, hard hoofs were transformed into spreading padded feet adapted for walking through soft sand. Camels are an essentially North American group, and their present distribution mainly as beasts of the Old World deserts is due to fairly recent developments.

Baluchitherium—a giant hornless rhinoceros (Oligocene and Miocene).

true pigs replaced the piglike entelodonts. In addition to these last, there were other piglike artiodactyls present during much of Tertiary time. One such Eurasian group, that of the **anthracotheres,** invaded North America during the Oligocene (e.g., *Bothriodon*), but they became extinct there during the Miocene (possibly because of oreodont competition). The anthracotheres showed early specializations for life in streams and along riverbanks—indeed, some of their last Pleistocene representatives in the Old World looked very much like hippopotamuses. True hippos do not appear until the Pliocene and their exact ancestry is not known, but it is thought that they might be an offshoot

Procamelus, a primitive Miocene camel adapted to the open prairie.

As already discussed, the primitive ruminants, the traguloids, continuing today as the little-changed Oriental chevrotains, were of Eurasian origin. Some of their middle Tertiary branches —such as the North American proto- ceratids—diverged widely from the generalized types but failed to survive. All the rest of the ruminants can be included in a single group—the **pec- orans.** They are the deer, the giraffes, and the **bovoids.** The last include pronghorns, sheep, goats, antelopes, and cattle. The deer can be considered the most primitive of the pecorans. They and the giraffes are closely allied and have a common ancestry in some of the Miocene stem deer. Most of the last (found both in Europe and North America) were small forms, with canine tusks instead of horns, and they appear to be related to certain of the Oligocene traguloids. There were some of these stem deer, however, that had horns of various types and arrangements. Among them was the little Miocene genus *Cranioceras.*

The bovoids are the most advanced of the ruminants, of particular interest to man since in addition to the antelopes they include most of his domesticated animals such as cattle, sheep, and goats. While the deer and giraffes are the browsers, the bovoids are the grazers among pecorans. They form a be- wildering array—widely distributed throughout the world. The horns pos- sessed by both males and females are permanent features and are not shed annually as are the male deer's. (There is one exception to this generalization: the American pronghorn bear's "decid- uous" horns.) The bovoids arose in Miocene times, probably from an Old World traguloid stock, but most of their evolutionary deployment has been confined to the Pliocene and later ages. They were of northern origin but southern Asia and Africa became the centres of their tremendous radiation, with a few of them (e.g., the pronghorns and bisons) reaching North America at

Phiomia, one of the first mastodonts.

With the rise of the cereals, harsh grasses spread a golden carpet across the plains of the world during the Miocene epoch, providing rich concentrated food for the animals that came out of the forests onto these wide open spaces. Beyond the two browsing mastodonts, a herd of early horses *(Merychippus)*

various times. (They never reached South America until introduced by man.) Sometime in the Pliocene true cattle evolved from certain north Eurasian cowlike antelopes, spreading extensively from there.

The Old World also seems to have been the centre of origin of the proboscideans—first the mastodonts and related forms and then the elephants derived from a mastodont stock. The two modern genera—each with a single species—that is, the African and the Asiatic elephant—are the lone survivors of a once prodigiously diversified middle-to-late Cenozoic assemblage. The early Oligocene proboscideans, descended from *Moeritherium*-like forms, seem to have undergone most of their initial evolution in what is now the valley of the Nile. By lower Oligocene times there already were present the first of the mastodonts, of which *Phiomia* is a good example. *Phiomia* was seven feet tall, with comparatively long legs and a typically high, swollen, elephantine skull.

is frolicking. To the far left are some long-necked early camels *(Alticamelus)*. The oddly horned ruminants are related to both deer and giraffes (*Syndyoceras* with little *Cranioceras* in front). In the water from right to left: a double-horned rhinoceros *(Diceratherium)*, and a giant piglike artiodactyl *(Dinohyus)*. Another of this last on land, and next to it are their three young.

It had a well-formed trunk (this can be told from the backward position of the nasal bones in the skull), and in front there were two tusks projecting forward and down—tusks derived from the enlarged second incisors of its ancestor. The lower jaw was very long and also carried in front of it two tusks which protruded horizontally. Forms such as this gave rise to the later mastodonts which successfully invaded the northern continents and were present throughout Eurasia and in North America before the end of the Miocene. There were two independent lines of mastodonts that evolved side by side all through the middle and late Cenozoic— the long-jawed forms, most of which bore long tusks on the lower jaws, and the short-jawed mastodonts, which from the outset of their history had virtually tuskless lower jaws. Some of the most remarkable of the long-jawed mastodonts were the so-called shovel-tuskers, of which the Pliocene North American genus *Amebelodon* is an example. Presumably the scoop formed by the broad, flattened tusks was used to dig up plants. The **rhynchotheres** (e.g., *Rhynchotherium*) were another long-jawed mastodont group which had the front of their lower jaws and tusks strongly downturned. The **dinotheres,** represented throughout their history by the single genus *Dinotherium,* were a completely independent proboscidean lineage. They first showed up, already highly specialized, in the Miocene and continued on in the Old World only until their extinction during the Pleistocene epoch. The Miocene species were of modest size compared to the late Cenozoic species of *Dinotherium,* some of which stood ten feet high. They had no upper ivories, but the lower jaws held two large hooklike tusks which curved strongly back towards the body. A really peculiar adaptation—quite difficult to interpret. (Perhaps these odd protuberances were used to rip up roots.) The elephants, distinguished from mastodonts by a highly specialized and distinct dentition, evolved from certain of the Miocene long-jawed mastodonts. By late Pliocene times there existed fully fledged elephants in which the upper tusks were long and curved and the lower jaw had become short and tuskless. Mammoths (a term simply signifying extinct elephants) became very widespread during the Pleistocene but never reached South America.

During middle- and late-Cenozoic times many lines of herbivorous animals were showing strong trends towards size increase. The grassy plains were expanding, and adaptations for grazing on the open prairies became the dominant feature. But evolution is never an isolated process—the carnivores still had to make a living, and they, too, sent forth their representatives from the forests and showed trends in size increase similar to the herbivores. One was acting as an evolutionary stimulus upon the other.

When the Eocene epoch came to an end some thirty-five million years ago, the great majority of the creodonts had become extinct, except for the hyaenodonts, which managed to survive into the early Pliocene. The fissiped carnivores derived from a miacid stock replaced the creodonts and became the dominant flesh eaters of subsequent times.

Carnivorous habits place great demand on intelligence, strength, and quickness. The herbivore has need to develop complicated teeth and digestive organs

Dinotherium, an Old World proboscidean (Miocene to Pleistocene)

Pliocene mastodonts in North America. In front, several shovel-tusked individuals belonging to the genus *Amebelodon*, and a herd of another kind of mastodont, *Rhynchotherium*, at the back.

to grind up and convert bulky plant food into energy; however, it generally has no problem in finding a rich source of nourishment. The carnivore usually does not require advanced specializations (of the "food-factory" kind characteristic of herbivores) but depends instead upon its ability to catch animals—its source of food being a much more uncertain proposition. It has to be able to creep up unobserved on a shy and watchful prey, then catch up with a terror-stricken nimble creature running for its life, and lastly it must have the strength to overcome and kill its victim. Competition for food among carnivores has consequently always been intense, and they have been obliged to develop not only large brains and wide-awake senses but also powerful limbs with sharp claws and efficient ripping, stabbing, and slicing teeth between muscular jaws.

As previously mentioned, by late Eocene-early Oligocene times the fissipeds were already evolving along two basic directions—one branch comprising the canoids or dog assemblage, and the other, the feloids or cat grouping.

The canoids fall into several related families: the **canids,** or dog clan proper; the **ursids,** or bears; the **procyonids,** or raccoons, kinkajous and pandas; and the **mustelids,** or weasel family.

Cynodictis was one of the first primitive canids. It was a weasel-like animal similar to the miacids, but it already showed the progressive trends characteristic of all later dogs. The limbs and feet were somewhat elongated; the carnassials (or slicing cheek teeth) were more specialized as shearing blades, and, most important, the brain case was expanded. From forms such as this, one central line of canid evolution led through the Oligocene and subsequent epochs to the Pleistocene and Recent dog genera such as man's best friend *Canis*. The reminder is probably superfluous by now, but this was anything but "straight-line" evolution—there were numerous side branches during Miocene and Pliocene times. Modern canids include the wild dogs, wolves, foxes, and fennecs of the northern hemisphere and also the highly specialized dogs of South America and Africa.

During the Miocene some dogs began to diverge in the evolutionary direction that led to the bears. These transitional groups tended to be large and heavy, and the late Miocene genus *Hemicyon* is typical. In later ursids the skull became more and more robust, the carnassials lost their shearing function, and all the cheek teeth became square and blunt. True bears had appeared by the Pliocene, and they evolved rapidly through the Pleistocene, becoming heavy-footed large ani-

mals, omnivorous rather than truly carnivorous in their feeding habits. Bears entered South America in the Pleistocene, but for unknown reasons they never invaded southern Africa.

Another evolutionary trend away from the "main" line of canid evolution was in the direction of the raccoons—or procyonids. As in bears, here, too, the new adaptations were not for the chase and the kill but rather for climbing and an omnivorous diet. The procyonids probably diverged from a canid stock during the Oligocene—by Miocene times they were well established. They are an essentially New World group (reaching South America from their centre of origin, North America), mainly forest dwellers with very catholic tastes. A procyonid branch that got into Eurasia developed into the pandas, one of which (the Chinese giant panda) has become a complete herbivore living exclusively on green bamboo shoots.

The weasel group, the mustelids, can be set apart (within the canoids) from the more closely interrelated dogs, bears, and raccoons. The mustelids have been a separate lineage from their original appearance in Oligocene times. Some of them have remained more or less primitive, retaining the characteristics of their middle-Tertiary ancestors—a good set of carnassials, a short face, a long, expanded brain case, and a relatively elongated body on short legs. This group includes the weasels, the martens, the minks, and the wolverines—all highly active, carnivorous, often semi-arboreal forest dwellers. Then there exist the more specialized mustelids—the large, heavy, burrowing, and omnivorous badgers, the small, ground-dwelling, notorious, and rather omnivorous skunks, and finally the aquatic fish-eating otters and mollusc-eating sea otters. Of all the carnivores, the mustelids show the widest range of adaptive radiation. Their high degree of intelligence makes most of them very appealing creatures.

On the feloid side of the fissiped carnivores stand the civets, hyenas, and cats. The Old World civets, including the genets and the renowned mongooses (which, by the way, do not specialize in killing and eating snakes any more than do many other small carnivores), are the most primitive. The civet family is known as the **viverrids,** and they are essentially late Eocene progressive miacids. In Miocene times, one branch diverged from the central civet stock and, in a continuous trend towards size increase and particularly towards the development of a heavy skull with enlarged jaws and robust teeth, gave rise to the **hyaenids.** Hyenas live in open areas and they have long limbs for running; their jaws have become particularly powerful in an adaptation for cracking the bones of large carcasses on which these carrion eaters feed.

The **felids,** or the cats proper, split off from the civet stock before the divergence of the hyaenid branch. By late Eocene times we already meet with transitional forms "pointing" towards the felids, and by the early Oligocene the cats were highly evolved, not much different from modern forms. The felids are the most completely adapted of all land-living carnivores for a killing and meat-eating existence. They have always come in all sizes—and the modern representatives such as "cat" cats, lynxes, jaguars, cougars, leopards, tigers, and lions are known to everyone. In general, all felids are very supple and muscular—with strong limbs adapted for short bursts of speed and long bounds. They have sharp retractile claws (in contrast to canids), and their teeth are perfect stabbing and cutting weapons. The smaller forms are good tree climbers. From the time of their definition in Oligocene times, and continuing through to the Pleistocene, the felids evolved along two lines. One was that of the "feline" cats, represented by all the modern felids and their ancestors (e.g., the Oligocene *Dinictis*); the other was the "sabre-tooth" lineage, descended from Oligocene forms such as *Hoplophoneus,* whose upper canine teeth were elongated into two-inch daggers. There was a flange on each side of the lower jaw to protect these powerful stabbing tools when the mouth was closed. In the evolution of "feline" cats the canine teeth became somewhat smaller than they had been on the Oligocene forms; in the sabre-tooths the canines remained large as in *Hoplophoneus.* The "felines" were the more nimble of the two cat lineages—adapted to catch and kill agile prey; they are the cats of Recent times. The sabre-tooths were specialized for killing large, heavy animals whose thick hides they could pierce with their sharp cutting daggers. As we shall see, the sabre cats became extinct in the late Pleistocene when most of their bulky prey died out.

The **seals,** and their relatives, which millions of years after the extinction of the plesiosaurs replaced these marine reptiles in the oceans of the world, are another branch of modern carnivores. They are called **pinnipeds** in contrast to the land-living fissiped flesh eaters. They do not appear in the fossil record until the Miocene—by that time already specialized for a marine existence. The pinnipeds include the sea lions, walruses, and seals, and probably they diverged from early fissipeds (possibly mustelid ancestors) in late-Eocene or early-Oligocene times. In their aquatic adaptations the pinnipeds never went as far as the whales (or earlier ichthyosaurs). They swim by actively using their paddlelike forelimbs, as well as by body movements. They come up on land, or onto ice floes, to breed, and the woolly young take a while before entering their parents' main element.

As the Miocene epoch drew towards its close, the "modernization" of mammals had proceeded very far along its way, and all over the earth life flourished in brilliant and already familiar complexity.

Among the rodents, the first true beavers, the mice and rats, and the stem porcupines had made their appearance during the Oligocene. Some of the last somehow got into isolated South America —possibly being rafted across from North America on floating logs. Once there, they radiated out into the South American porcupines, the guinea pigs, the agoutis, and the chinchillas. The early beavers were small, burrowing rodents and only later became specialized for an aquatic existence. Mice and their relatives, such

as voles and lemmings, are probably the most numerous of all mammals. The success of the rodents in general has been a truly phenomenal one—helped greatly by the agricultural and carnivore-eliminating activities of man in recent times.

The lagomorphs, or hares and rabbits, had also become abundant by the Oligocene.

Up in the treetops the primates, too, had been branching out. Among the advanced primates, or anthropoids, the Oligocene genus *Parapithecus,* found in Egypt, is the oldest known Old World monkey. It was a rather small monkey and has been regarded by some scientists as an early ape. Perhaps it is the common ancestor from which later monkeys and apes arose. The New World monkeys have an even poorer fossil record, and our first record of them is from the Miocene. The living forms differ from Old World monkeys in many features, particularly in the use of their prehensile tails

An Oligocene creodont (*Hyaenodon*) caught unawares by an early sabre-tooth cat (*Hoplophoneus*). A hare (*Palaeolagus*) skips away to the right.

as a "third hand" while climbing. Associated with *Parapithecus,* in the same Oligocene sediments, there was also found *Propliopithecus,* which from certain features of the jaw and dentition appears to be a forerunner of both the gibbon line and also of the **dryopithecines.** These last were generalized Miocene apes who are thought to have been ancestral to the other apes (the chimpanzees, gorillas, and orangs) as well as to the African man-apes who will be discussed later.

But of course the mammals were not alone in their possession of the earth. The reptiles were represented by many kinds of lizards, primitive constrictors as well as advanced poisonous snakes, crocodilians, and turtles. (The chelonians are really very successful animals—there are terrestrial, fresh-water, and marine species, and, although size is no true indication of evolutionary success, they too have had and still have their giants.) Amphibians in the guise of frogs, toads, and salamanders were occupying the same niches they do today, usually adapted to life near the edge of streams and ponds. Middle- to late-Tertiary birds are known mainly from fragmentary bones, but it is clear that their present-day distribution and adaptive radiation had already been fully established—there were forest and upland forms, song birds, birds of prey, wading and shore birds, and even fully aquatic types like the penguins. During Miocene times, in South America, there strutted long-legged, flightless *Phororhacos,* the height of a man, with a powerful beaked skull as large as that of a horse. Possibly this ground-living carnivorous bird competed with the marsupial flesh eaters of that continent.

And disregarding the vertebrates for a while and turning instead to the inverte-brates, the latter's conquest of the earth and air, particularly demonstrated by the modern types of insects, has been a continuously expanding success story from the Jurassic on.

Although laurels and magnolia trees were still growing in Greenland at the end of the Miocene, the trend towards progressive cooling that had until now marked the entire course of the Cenozoic was beginning to reach its climax. In the higher latitudes the summers were getting too short and too cool to melt all the snow that had fallen during the long winters, and slowly the ice masses were collecting on the high mountains of Greenland, Siberia, and Scandinavia.

A few million years later chilly gusts of wind were blowing over the northern plains to give warning of the coming Ice Age.

A giant flightless bird of prey *(Phororacos;* Miocene; South America).

THE GREAT FROST

The final epoch of the Tertiary period, the Pliocene, lasted about ten million years, and it was followed by the four glacial periods of the Pleistocene.

Throughout the greater part of the Pliocene the climate remained relatively mild, but towards its end the north wind began to bite more sharply and the vegetation gradually changed character. The coniferous forests moved down the sides of the mountains, and the monotonous gloom of spruces and pines replaced the more colourful deciduous flora along the slopes of the river valleys.

And on the heels of the conifers came the ice.

For century after century, millennium after millennium, the ice masses of the North crept southward until they covered more than a quarter of the surface of the continents, and millions of square miles of Europe and North America were transformed into snowy wastelands. On all the mountain peaks of the world, even in Africa and tropical Central America, tremendous ice caps were formed, and from the Alps, the Himalayas, and other mountains the glaciers spread down over the surrounding lowlands. When the cold was at its height, the glaciers of Scandinavia were only some three hundred miles distant from the Alps and the greater part of the intervening territory was deep frozen tundra. In North America the great ice sheets spread from Greenland down over what are now the Great Lakes, as far south as New Jersey and Pennsylvania in the east, and also below the Canadian border to the west. Parts of this frozen sheet were thousands of feet thick.

But the Pleistocene was not a permanent ice winter. It had long intervening periods of warm weather during which the glaciers retreated to their sources while tropical and subtropical animals and plants once more took possession of the reclaimed land. The Recent—the geological epoch in which we are living today—began some ten to fifteen thousand years ago with the start of the fourth and most recent retreat of the ice. We call the Recent the "post-glacial period", but it might be more correctly designated as the fourth interglacial period of the Great Ice Age.

The reasons behind the tremendous glaciations are unknown and have given rise to many speculations. Various theories, so far unproven, have been set up, among them that glacial periods are due to variations in the intensity of the heat given off by the sun or to changes in the angle of inclination of the earth's axis. The existence of high mountain ranges also appears to be a factor—since glaciers first form locally on chilly heights, cause a drop in surrounding temperatures, and then creep downward and over the plains. Although the causes of climatic fluctua-

An American sabre-tooth has just torn down *Synthetoceras*, a deerlike Pliocene ruminant with a peculiar Y-shaped horn on its nose.

tions are not fully understood, we do know that an average drop in world temperatures of as little as 8° Centigrade would lead to renewed glaciation of an extent equal to the four previous Pleistocene events. Also, it is estimated that the complete melting of all the still existing glacier ice would return enough water to the sea to raise its level about a hundred feet. This would drown vast areas of land, submerging cities such as New York, Boston, London, and Hamburg in the process. Since glaciers were much more extensive previously, the level of the sea in those past times is thought to have been three hundred feet below what it is now. The rapid wastage of existing ice masses under the warm conditions of our period is causing the level of the sea to rise about two and a half inches per century.

There is no doubt, if past events are actually repeating themselves (and we really don't know that they are), that a catastrophic future is in store for our most densely populated areas, first from flooding and later from the creeping cold.

During Pliocene times the trend towards the establishment of Recent faunas continued without interruption, leading smoothly into the Pleistocene representatives of all the animals now present. Many lines were continuing to send out branches that culminated in Pleistocene giants, most of them now extinct, as well as giving us our familiar contemporaneous mammals.

A relatively primitive group of originally Miocene rodents gave rise to an offshoot which in Pliocene times had members, such as *Epigaulus* of North America, with horns on the skull. These were the only rodents which ever showed this type of specialization.

Camels were among the commonest artiodactyls on the prairies of North America, and some of them by now looked very much like their modern descendants. Mastodonts flourished on both sides of the Atlantic, and some of them

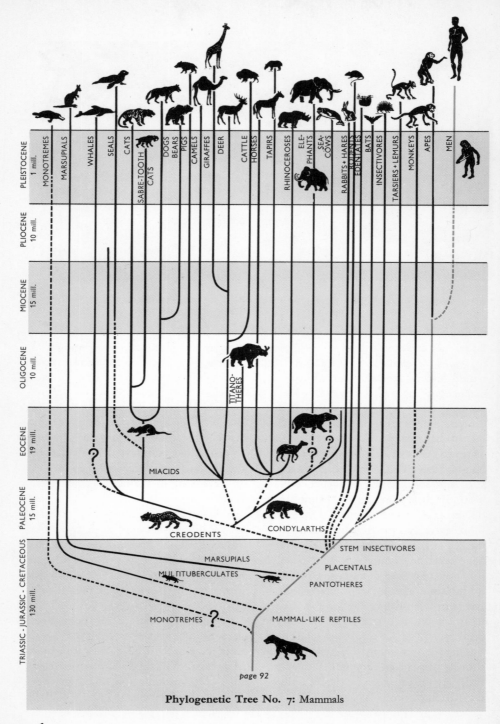

Phylogenetic Tree No. 7: Mammals

MONOTREMES · MARSUPIALS · WHALES · SEALS · CATS · SABRE-TOOTH CATS · DOGS · BEARS · PIGS · CAMELS · GIRAFFES · DEER · CATTLE · HORSES · TAPIRS · RHINOCEROSES · ELEPHANTS · SEA-COWS · RABBITS + HARES · RODENTS · EDENTALS · BATS · INSECTIVORES · TARSIERS + LEMURS · MONKEYS · APES · MEN

PLEISTOCENE 1 mill.

PLIOCENE 10 mill.

MIOCENE 15 mill.

OLIGOCENE 10 mill.

EOCENE 19 mill.

PALEOCENE 15 mill.

TRIASSIC · JURASSIC · CRETACEOUS 130 mill.

TITANO-THERES

MIACIDS

CREODENTS

CONDYLARTHS

STEM INSECTIVORES

MARSUPIALS

PLACENTALS

MULTITUBERCULATES

PANTOTHERES

MONOTREMES ?

MAMMAL-LIKE REPTILES

page 92

146

Epigaulus, a member of the only horned group among the rodents. Next to it, *Pratilepus,* a Pliocene lagomorph or hare.

were developing into elephants in the Old World. By the end of the Pliocene the first elephants had appeared, and soon they, too, invaded North America.

At the beginning of the Pliocene an event of consequence was taking place. The horse returned to the Old World where its original ancestors *(Hyracotherium)* had long since died out and where the heavy forest-dwelling horses derived from the late Oligocene North American genus *Miohippus* were already becoming extinct. These invaders were of the genus *Hipparion,* descended from the North American genus *Merychippus. Hipparion* was extremely common on both sides of the Bering land bridge in early Pliocene times. It was a lightly built grazing horse, progressive in its dentition, but conservative in the development of the limbs— *Hipparion* had remained a three-toed horse. *Hipparion* lingered on in Africa until Pleistocene times but became extinct in Eurasia and North America at the end of the Pliocene. However, another descendant of *Merychippus,* the strictly North American late Miocene to late Pliocene genus *Pliohippus,* became the direct ancestor of *Equus,* the modern horse (as well as of a now extinct South American genus). *Pliohippus* not only had advanced high-crowned grazing teeth,

Pliohippus. A herd of the immediate forerunners of the horse we know today.

but it also had greatly reduced side toes that were no longer functional. *Equus* arose in North America towards the very end of the Pliocene, continuing all the trends typical for *Pliohippus* (the modern horse still has two vestigial side toes concealed beneath the skin of the foot). *Equus* migrated across the Bering bridge and also into South America at the beginning of the Pleistocene, but it became extinct in the New World a few thousand years ago. In the meantime it had filled the steppes of Asia, Europe, and Africa with a great variety of different species that we call horses, zebras, and asses.

Another group of perissodactyls, the rhinoceroses, also died out in North America—well before the disappearance of horses from that continent. Rhinos had already become extinct in the New World by the end of the Pliocene. At the same time most of them died out in Eurasia—and they are now a vanishing group represented by a very few Asiatic and African species.

North America also witnessed the disappearance of its camels, mastodonts, elephants, and tapirs, but before these impoverishing events took place, the Panama isthmus had once again risen from the depths and re-established the connection between North and South America. This occurred towards the end of the Pliocene, and thereafter all the continents with the exception of Australia remained joined in a roundabout fashion via the various land bridges. Of course, it must be remembered that, as climatic conditions became extreme in northern areas, a bridge like the Bering Strait passage would only permit forms accustomed to arctic and temperate zone

The Panama isthmus became a firm land bridge again at the close of the Tertiary period, during the late Pliocene epoch. From the south came herbivores such as giant ground sloths and glyptodonts.

conditions to cross—tropical forms would be barred.

Ice sheets are built up of atmospheric moisture, precipitated chiefly in the form of snow and derived ultimately by evaporation from the sea. It follows that the greater the amount of moisture locked up on land in the form of ice and snow, the less water there is left in the sea. Consequently, with the building up of tremendous masses of snow and ice in the mountainous regions of the world, towards the end of the Pliocene, the level of the oceans began to drop, and the Panama land bridge, after having been submerged from early Tertiary times on, reappeared from below the waves.

For the placental ungulates and marsupial carnivores of South America, until then isolated, this was to prove a fateful event. Hordes of North American advanced fissiped carnivores, such as large wild dogs, foxes, bears, and various cats, including sabre-tooths, mountain lions, and jaguars, streamed down into South America. With them arrived northern ungulates such as tapirs, horses, deer, llamas (a camel offshoot), and mastodonts. The indigenous South American herbivores had done well enough in defending themselves against the attacks of carnivorous marsupials, but they were simply not adapted to withstand advanced placental beasts of prey. That was a primary cause of their almost total extinction within a short space of time after the re-emergence of the Panama isthmus. A secondary cause was competition for living space and food from the incoming northern perissodactyls, artiodactyls, and proboscideans. Only a few large specialized South American ungulates survived,

In turn, South America was invaded by intelligent progressive carnivores such as large wild dogs and sabre-tooth cats from the north.

among them the notoungulate *Toxodon,* which continued into the Pleistocene. The coming of the northern placental carnivores also sounded the death knell of the marsupial flesh eaters, until then very successful. Some of the latter had by Pliocene times evolved into tiger-sized animals with upper canine blades almost exactly like those of placental sabre cats (a remarkable case of convergence). However, in spite of such advanced specializations, competition from the more intelligent and reproductively more efficient placental carnivores was too much, and all these marsupials became extinct.

The reader will remember that there was another isolated group evolving in South America during Tertiary times— that of the edentates (an order of placental mammals). Many of these showed trends towards giantism. For example, there evolved among the sloths, giant ground sloths like *Megatherium,* twenty feet long and weighing several tons. The ground sloths were probably plant eaters, living on the leaves of trees and bushes. The armadillos too had giant cousins, the **glyptodonts,** often ten feet long and encased in a solid impenetrable body armour. They wore bony helmets, and the tip of the armoured tail ended in a mace-like club. (Here is a case of "belated" convergence towards the long extinct armoured dinosaurs—the ankylosaurs). With the re-establishment of the isthmian link the highly specialized edentates, almost alone among the native South American animals, successfully withstood the consequent invasion from the north. They not only held their ground, but they "infiltrated behind the enemy lines" and spread into Central and North America. The glyptodonts and giant ground sloths ranged widely during Pleistocene times in both North and South America, and there is evidence that these mammals survived until comparatively late dates. Early man in the New World was contemporaneous with ground sloths, whose partial mummies with patches of skin and hair intact have been discovered several times.

The other representatives of the sloth group—the tree sloths and the anteaters —never got north of the tropical region, but the armadillos entered the southern portion of North America and are to this day steadily extending their range northward. The armour of the modern armadillos, as contrasted to that of the now extinct glyptodonts, is a flexible one, and they can roll themselves up into a ball for protection. They are extremely adaptable animals, nocturnal in their habits, feeding on carrion, insects, or any food that may come their way. Some of them have the peculiar reproductive habit of bearing only identical quadruplets.

Others among the South American natives who were little affected by the northern invasion were the indigenous rodents (the porcupines even staged a "counter-attack"), monkeys, and opossums.

Elephants never got across the isthmus, but several mastodonts did, and among the smaller mammals numerous mice and lagomorphs also established themselves in South America.

During the interglacial periods the climatic zonal boundaries shifted even farther north than they are today, so that essentially tropical conditions were to be found over great parts of Europe and North America. The fauna occurring in these regions, during the three interglacial stages, in many respects resembled

A mighty giant bison and a dire wolf. In the background some modern horses, and Pleistocene *Gigantocamelus,* one of the last representatives of the camels in North America.

present-day animal life in tropical Africa.

In the Pleistocene representatives of all the types now present were common. In addition, there were numerous animals now extinct—and most of these last were giants.

Packs of giant wolves (dire wolves) yapped around the teeming buffalo herds of the prairies. There were North American **bison** measuring over six feet from horntip to horntip. Certain deer, like the giant **Irish elk,** carried antlers spanning twelve feet across. Giant beavers the size of small bears lived in both North America and Europe. They were masterful engineers and built impressive dams across the rivers. Even in isolated Australia there were giant kangaroos,

giant marsupial carnivores, and, of all things, an unusually large platypus.

A Pleistocene sabre-tooth (*Smilodon*) was bigger and heavier than any "feline" tiger living today—well able to tear down the large tuskers it preyed on. During the interglacial periods the modern lion spread over the greater part of Europe, and at the same time the cougar or puma ranged widely through the Americas. The majority of present-day carnivores—foxes, raccoons, weasels, otters, hyenas, the smaller felines, etc.— had made their appearance.

The steppes resounded to the hoof beat of horses, camels, and wild cattle. Elephants and hippopotamuses grazed along the banks of the river Somme in

Over much of North America and Eurasia luxuriant savannah and forested regions were transformed into barren polar wastes before the advancing glaciers formed during the cold phases of the great Ice Age. Many forms were driven from these regions, but many others were able to adapt successfully to the rigorous environment. A long-haired mammoth is here shown against the green glacier edge

France, and rhinoceroses migrated as far north as Denmark.

Today practically all of the big animals are gone. A few survive in Africa and tropical southeastern Asia, but in the rest of the world they disappeared around the close of the Pleistocene in the same sudden, abrupt manner as the dinosaurs of the Cretaceous period had done about seventy million years previously. The reason for this widespread extinction is as much of a mystery as is that of the ruling reptiles at the end of the Mesozoic.

The flourishing animal life of North America was possibly the hardest hit. The horse became extinct and did not return to the New World until around the year 1500, together with the Spanish conquistadores. The North American camels had sent the llama to South America, while other camels migrated to Asia, where they are still found. But in North America, their "homeland", there have been no camels for many thousands of years. (A giant Pleistocene genus *Giganto-camelus* was one of the last native camels.) The mastodonts and mammoths, and with them the sabre cats, also vanished. So did the ground sloths and the glyptodonts.

During the Ice Age, Europe was for long periods extensively connected to Africa, either across the Straits of Gibraltar or by way of the Italian peninsula via Sicily and Malta. Also, there were wide traversable routes between the Oriental region and North Africa. During the glacial periods European and Asian hippopotamuses, rhinoceroses, elephants, antelopes, horses, and various carnivores were able to escape across these land bridges and migrate back again the same way, when a new rise in world temperatures caused the ice masses to retreat.

of the inland ice sheet, flanked by a musk ox on the left and a woolly rhinoceros on the right. In the foreground, a polar fox dashes away, and, behind, a herd of migrating reindeer trots along.

153

They spent their "exile" in North Africa, which during the Pleistocene was not a desert but a luxuriant savannah abounding with wild life and dotted with lakes and intersected by big rivers. The region which is now the Sahara and Arabian desert had plentiful rainfall during the cold spells up north. With the retreat of the glaciers atmospheric-pressure zones shifted, and the rain-bearing winds dropped their condensed moisture over central Europe instead of farther south. Apparently desert conditions between Europe and South Africa (and also in the southwestern United States) always prevail during interglacial stages.

As the ice sheets crept southward, so did the tropical fauna—well in advance. However, this did not leave now mostly arctic Eurasia and North America barren of animal life. Even during the greatest extremes of cold the tundras of the world supported a relatively abundant and varied arctic fauna. It was merely a different type of animal life.

Each time the glaciers started moving, the cold-adapted animals of the polar regions were able to extend their range southward into formerly subtropical and tropical areas. Among these strictly arctic types were **musk oxen, reindeer, lemmings,** and **polar foxes.** The last mentioned reached the Danube; reindeer penetrated south of the Pyrenees, and lemmings have been traced down as far as southern Portugal.

Some of what are now wholly tropical groups developed species adapted to arctic conditions. There were **woolly rhinoceroses** in Eurasia, and even the proboscideans gave rise to an arctic representative—the mighty **woolly mammoth**—which, until the very end of the Pleistocene, lived on the tundras of northern Eurasia and North America. From frozen carcasses found in both Siberia and Alaska we know that this polar elephant had a dense coat of long rusty-red hair, and although not as big as other contemporary proboscideans, the woolly mammoth had remarkably long, curved tusks.

Among the rugged peaks and mountain passes of Europe there lived enormous **cave bears,** a giant race of the common brown bear and, as were all of these late Pleistocene animals, a contemporary of early man.

It would be giving too much credit to the decimating ability of primitive man to imagine that the late Pleistocene extinctions were due to his doing, but there is no doubt that mammoths, cave bears, and rhinos, among others, were successfully hunted by that primate with the outsize brain—man—who had put in his appearance sometime before the first half of the Ice Age was over.

Giant Pleistocene beavers *(Castoroides),* as large as small bears.

154

The oldest traces of the first true men date from early- to middle-Pleistocene times, but already during the Miocene epoch (if not before) the human line must have split off from that leading to the modern anthropoid apes.

The previously mentioned Miocene hominoids (the grouping including both apes and men)—the **dryopithecines**—represented by *Proconsul* (from Africa) and its later descendants such as *Dryopithecus* and other genera (from Europe, Asia, and Africa), are probably the group which some time during the Miocene gave rise to the evolutionary lineage which led to man. The dryopithecines were rather generalized primates, not particularly adapted to a life of brachiation. This last is the typical mode of progression of modern apes who swing from branch to branch by means of their powerful, elongated arms. The dryopithecines did not show any such specialization in their upper limbs; their posture when walking must have been

Left: a female *Sinanthropus* (Peking Man). Right: a male *Pithecanthropus* (Java Man).

essentially quadrupedal. In their skull and dentition, also, they possessed generalized features which could conceivably have led to both modern apes as one development and mankind as the other. In the latter, the **hominids,** as contrasted with the former, the **pongids,** evolution particularly emphasized adaptations for walking on the ground, rather than features which make for a primarily arboreal type of existence. The tremendous increase in brain size, so very characteristic of mankind, was actually a much later development—the typical erect pos-

South African australopithecines who might possibly have known the use of fire and who hunted big game.

ture and walking mechanism of hominids becoming "perfected" much earlier.

That the two hominid characteristics, erect bipedal locomotion and an enlarged brain, did not evolve simultaneously but were distinct in their respective rates of evolution, one lagging behind the other, is clearly demonstrated by the **australopithecines,** recently discovered in South African Pleistocene cave deposits. These, the so-called "southern apes", were very remarkable creatures. In their limb structure they were clearly hominids, but in their skulls they were rather primitive, with a small brain capacity and large jaws. They were about four feet tall, fully erect, and adapted for a terrestrial rather than a climbing and brachiating mode of life. Their dentition, too, was more human than it was apelike, and in spite of their small brains they appear to be hominoids that have clearly evolved in the hominid rather than the pongid direction. There are really no linking forms (unless the very recently discovered complete skeletons of *Oreopithecus* from late Miocene-early Pliocene beds in Italy can be demonstrated to have belonged to such a transitional group), but it seems reasonable to suppose that the Pleistocene australopithecines were descended from Miocene dryopithecines. The big question, of course, is whether these African man-apes are ancestral to any of the primitive but definitely human fossils that have been found in both Java and China—the **pithecanthropoids.** Historically they are too late in time to be on the direct line leading to humans, since most of the pithecanthropoid finds are no more recent than the australopithecine discoveries. However, structurally they represent a real stage in hominid evolution—the australopithecines

are probably a side branch that remained more or less primitive into the Pleistocene, while some of their close relatives went on to evolve up to the pithecanthropoid level.

Another obvious question that occurs about the African man-apes is whether they were human to the extent of having possessed some sort of culture; that is, were they capable of speech and did they make tools? The first question remains unanswerable, but the second can possibly be answered in the affirmative. From crushed baboon skulls that have been found it appears likely that the australopithecines did use instruments of some sort to kill the animals they hunted. One scientist even goes so far as to claim that certain marks on nearby rocks are the result of charring and that the man-apes knew the use of fire. However, this is extremely vague evidence and must be taken with a grain of salt.

The first true men, the pithecanthropoids, are represented by *Pithecanthropus* from Java **(Java Man),** *Sinanthropus* from China **(Peking Man),** and probably also **Heidelberg Man** (only a jaw exists) from Europe. (The recently discovered *Atlanthropus* from North Africa also appears to be a pithecanthropoid.) These can all be dated as having lived from early- to middle-Pleistocene times, and they are probably of an australopithecine-like ancestry. The minor differences between all these fossils would in any other animal not be accorded generic status, but due to the importance attached, reasonably enough, by modern man to his ancestors, every fossil is studied exceptionally closely, and even the smallest details are felt to be significant. Actually all the pithecanthropoids should be included in one genus, namely *Pithecanthropus*. *Pithe-*

Early European representative of the genus *Homo* (to which our species *Homo sapiens* belongs), engaged in combat with a cave bears.

canthropus was still primitive in its relatively small brain size (somewhat below that of modern man), in its heavy brow ridges, and also in its strong, forwardly projecting chinless jaw. But it was definitely a ground-living human and very likely knew the use of fire. It made primitive tools of wood and stone (these have been found in association with pithecanthropoid fossils).

All men other than *Pithecanthropus* can be placed into the genus *Homo*. The first representative of the genus to which we belong was **Neanderthal Man,** who lived in the Old World (Europe, Asia, and Africa) during and after the third interglacial period in late Pleistocene times. It used to be believed that Neanderthal Man led to *Homo sapiens* or modern man, but this theory has now been somewhat modified. It appears that the so-called "classical" Neanderthal Man—typically a short, stocky human with stooped shoulders, heavy brow ridges, and a

receding chin—was a specialized offshoot from a more "generalized" type which led to *Homo sapiens* as one of its developments. These more generalized humans are known from fossils that predate the "classical" Neanderthal finds.

The first known representative of *Homo sapiens* was **Cro-Magnon Man,** who is believed to have originated in Asia and whose distinctive culture appears in Europe near the close of the Old Stone Age, some fifty thousand years ago. Cro-Magnon Man was indistinguishable from modern Europeans, and he is thought to have displaced Neanderthal Man and possibly interbred with him in certain regions such as the Near East. He lived in rock shelters and caves, made chipped-stone instruments and weapons, and drew wonderful pictures of the animals that lived around him. He, and to a somewhat lesser extent Neanderthal Man before him, had a complex culture: hunting bears, wolves, great cats, rhinos, and

Neanderthal Man.

mammoths; worshiping his gods and burying his dead with pomp and ceremony.

Man was essentially an Old World development, but towards the close of the Pleistocene, and after, mankind spread over the globe. Asiatic *Homo sapiens,* at a Cro-Magnon level of culture, invaded the New World via the Bering land bridge to populate North and South America, some fifteen to twenty thousand years ago. Other humans spread from Asia into the East Indies and the Pacific islands.

There are four basic stocks of modern man, among which the Australian aborigines are the most restricted geographically. The other three races are the caucasoids or whites, the negroids or Negroes, and the mongoloids or the Asiatics and the American Indians. All living men belong to the same species — *Homo sapiens.* The interbreeding Mendelian populations that constitute the races of mankind (just as they do the races within other animal species) have never been constant in their isolation but have always shifted and interbred to some extent throughout mankind's history. If this were not the case, we would not get the fully fertile, perfectly normal offspring obtained today from any interracial cross. Men certainly differ from one another in their cultures, but they share and have shared, to varying degrees, a common gene pool.

As the only creatures capable of appreciating our own existence in terms of wanting to fathom the historical processes that have led to what we see around us, humans stand alone. The ability to pass on knowledge from generation to generation and thereby build a cumulative culture is unknown in other animals —at least to the degree that this ability is developed in mankind. And the symbols of our language are the tools that have given us this unique power.

Our story naturally ends with ourselves, but, if nothing else, this account should have made it clear that we are but one result among many. We are neither the beginning nor the end. The thread that has wound and twisted its way from the first glimmerings of life is still unravelling.

It is carried onward by the little field mouse, heavy with young, that seeks refuge among the stubble in the cornfields; by the air-borne seed vessels of the thistle that float on the summer breeze; by the young pregnant woman you meet in the street. The field mouse, the plant seed, and the woman all carry perpetuity in their wombs—that spark of life which since the beginning has been handed down from generation to generation like a never-extinguished torch.

INDEX

As the connection between present-day animals and extinct forms can often be of interest, the names of many modern animals whose development is described in the text have been included in this index. Page numbers printed in italics as a rule refer to an illustration only, but in several instances the reference is double, i.e. also to the text on the page in question.

160